CONTENTS

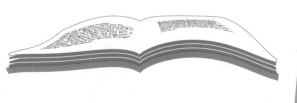

Scottish Book Trust
inspiring readers and writers

Changing lives through reading and writing

Scottish Book Trust is a national charity that believes books, reading and writing have the power to change lives.

A love of reading inspires creativity, improves employment opportunities, mental health and wellbeing, and is one of the most effective ways to help children escape the poverty cycle.

Working with Scottish Government, Creative Scotland and funding from individuals, companies, trusts and foundations, we deliver life changing programmes to people in need.

- Bookbug gifts books to every baby and child in Scotland to promote bonding and lay the building blocks of literacy, supported by an outreach programme for vulnerable families

- Read, Write, Count and the First Minister's Reading Challenge tackle the attainment gap for primary school age children, encourage reading for pleasure and support parents and teachers to understand the value of reading to a child's future

- We bring the excitement of live author events to hospitals, schools, youth projects and more, all across Scotland, driving a passion for reading

- Book Week Scotland celebrates reading Scotland-wide each November

- We inspire and support teens to develop their writing skills

- Our children's book prizes promote Scottish children's books and the people behind them to children all over the nation

We work towards a Scotland where everyone has an equal opportunity to thrive through literacy. Find out more at
scottishbooktrust.com
f /scottishbktrust 🐦 @scottishbktrust

FOREWORD

I love reading. I have loved reading all of my life. As long as I can remember – on car journeys and rainy school holidays – I've needed no excuse to delve into a book. These days, I have less time, but I know that reading inspired me during my childhood. And I know what a love of reading led to in terms of opportunities in my life.

So, I want to try and make sure more children get that opportunity too with the First Minister's Reading Challenge.

From this autumn, Scottish Book Trust will encourage children in schools across Scotland to go on their own reading journeys and challenge themselves to explore different types of books. My hope is that the First Minister's Reading Challenge will play a big part in encouraging children to catch the bug for reading. If they do, we hope they'll keep reading for life.

Research shows that reading for fun and personal enjoyment is hugely important for a child's success at school, which is why I am especially delighted that every child in Primaries 4 to 7 will have the opportunity to take part, further their reading skills, and hopefully develop a life-long passion of their own.

This is the start of something I want to see grow and grow in the years ahead.

So I really hope you all get the chance to be involved in the First Minister's Reading Challenge. Happy reading everyone!

Nicola Sturgeon
First Minister

THE LIST

Scotland's leading kids events guide.

We've got it covered

list.co.uk

CONTRIBUTORS

Editor: Lynsey May

Design: Lucy Munro, Carys Tennant

Subeditor: Paul McLean

Compilation of book list: Scottish Book Trust, with special thanks to everyone who fed into the selection process

Illustrations: Heedi Design

THE LIST
CEO: Simon Dessain
Publisher: Robin Hodge
Editor: Yasmin Sulaiman
Accounts: Sarah Reddie

Published in August 2016 by The List Ltd
Head Office:
14 High Street
Edinburgh EH1 1TE
Tel: 0131 550 3050
list.co.uk

Extensive efforts have been made to ensure the accuracy of the information in this publication; however the publishers cannot accept responsibility for any errors it may contain.

ISBN: 978-0-9557513-8-7

Printed by Stephens & George

'The whole world
opened up to me when
I learned to read'

- Mary McLeod Bethune

INTRODUCTION

D eveloping a love of books and reading – becoming a reader – is one of the very best things that can happen to a person. For children especially the benefits are immeasurable and lifelong, providing a firm foundation for a person's future wellbeing, achievements and enjoyment of life. Reading for pleasure, an activity open to us all equally, helps children in every area of life. On one hand it enhances the literacy and communication skills that are so central to any educational attainment; on the other it contributes to social and emotional development, allowing children to identify, articulate and process their feelings, to develop empathy for others, and to become socially sophisticated. These life skills are among the most important we can acquire. In allowing us to realise, develop and use these skills, reading helps us towards a life of opportunity, choice and personal fulfilment.

This is why initiatives that allow children to explore the fun and pleasure of reading are so important, and why developing a reading culture in schools and families is such a healthy, beneficial and worthwhile thing to do. If recent research has shown that children spend less leisure time reading for pleasure as they progress through school, it has also demonstrated that reading remains, across all age groups, our most widespread and valued cultural activity. In a digital age it is crucial that we continue to promote the transformative experience of reading to children, and find ways to make it accessible to, and enjoyable for, all.

Teaching a child to read does not make them a reader. It's the pleasure each child finds in a book that does. Every child's reading journey is valuable and unique, and is to be nurtured and encouraged in its own way. The authors, teachers, booksellers and learning professionals who made the wide spread of choices found here were guided by this thought, and two simple criteria – quality and enjoyability. The result is a list of truly great reads which will help children of all abilities and interests get started on their reading journey. We hope that journey lasts a lifetime. We hope they become readers.

Marc Lambert
CEO, Scottish Book Trust

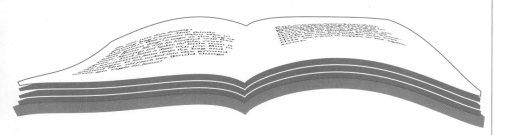

THE CAMPAIGN

The First Minister's Reading Challenge is an exciting new reading initiative for P4–7 children in schools across Scotland, delivered by Scottish Book Trust on behalf of the Scottish Government. Reading has the power to change lives and developing a love of reading in childhood can have a huge impact on educational attainment and future wellbeing. The First Minister wants to make sure every child in Scotland has an equal opportunity to experience the huge benefits that reading for pleasure brings.

The First Minister's Reading Challenge aims to build on the work already taking place in schools across the country to encourage children to read widely, explore a range of books and develop a love of reading. The main focus of the Challenge is to encourage reading for pleasure and support schools, libraries and communities to build reading cultures.

Children in P4–7 in every school in Scotland will be invited to take part in the Challenge. There is a dedicated Reading Challenge website where schools can register classes and where children, teachers and parents can find book suggestions, information, ideas and resources to encourage young people to develop a love of reading.

There will be a range of prizes awarded for schools and pupils to celebrate their reading journeys. The Challenge will also give the opportunity for every child's personal reading achievements to be celebrated by their teachers, librarians and parents.

This guide contains a list of recommended book suggestions to inspire young people to start their reading journey, and to signpost them on to other books that they might enjoy. Remember you can access a wide range of free books in all sorts of formats from your local library, as well as advice and recommendations from library staff.

'The more that you read, the more things you will know. The more that you learn, the more places you'll go'

- I Can Read With My Eyes Shut, Dr Seuss

As part of the First Minister's Reading Challenge, Scottish Book Trust has worked with a wide range of teachers, librarians, booksellers, authors and other professionals to create a list of 100 high-quality children's books, with each suggestion accompanied by two additional titles from the same genre.

With so many children's titles to choose from, this list can never include them all. It is simply a starting point, designed to motivate children to start a reading journey or encourage them to explore further. It includes classics and newer titles, non-fiction and graphic novels, and is organised by category, showcasing a breadth of exciting children's books to inspire as many children as possible. The books on the list are suggestions only. Children can take part in the Challenge and read entirely different books.

There is a book out there for everyone. The library or bookshop are the very best places to find your child's perfect book match, and to help broaden their reading tastes.

Once your children, class or group have discovered some titles that they love, why not consider putting together a reading list of their own and sharing it on our website? *www.readingchallenge.scot*

Funny

CIRCUS OF THIEVES AND THE RAFFLE OF DOOM
William Sutcliffe & David Tazzyman
(Simon & Schuster)

Hannah is bored. So very bored that when Armitage Shank's Impossible Circus rolls into town, she can hardly believe her luck. Packed with lively and hilarious characters, the circus quickly banishes boredom and turns her normal life upside down.

She makes friends with Billy Shank and his astonishing camel, Narcissus, and meets lots of terrific and talented performers. But something is not as it should be and soon Hannah and Billy realise that it's up to them to get to the bottom of the ringmaster's dastardly deeds.

If you've ever thought about how cool it would be to run away and join the circus, this fabulously funny book might just change your mind! Armitage Shank knows how to put on one great show, but he's also a deliciously bad baddie and an out and out thief – good thing Hannah, Billy and a bunch of wacky characters are there to save the day.
■ *Martha MacDiarmid, Animation Producer*

IF YOU LIKE THIS, WHY NOT TRY . . .

MR GUM
Andy Stanton & David Tazzyman

TUMTUM AND NUTMEG: A CIRCUS ADVENTURE
Emily Bearn

MR MINGIN (MR STINK IN SCOTS)
David Walliams & Quentin Blake (Translated by Matthew Fitt)
(Black & White Publishing)

'Mr Mingin minged. He monged tae. And if it is guid Scots tae say he mingit, then he mingit as weel. He wis the mingiest mingin minger that ever lived.'

Twelve-year-old Chloe is lonely, she's also having a tough time at school and at home. Then she makes friends with Mr Mingin, the local tramp, and things start to change.

There's more to Mr Mingin than meets the eye. When it looks as if he may be chased out of town, unbeknown to the rest of her family, Chloe gives him a home in the garden shed. My son and I laughed and laughed reading this book together. At its core, it is a heartwarming tale of friendship with a surprise twist at the end, and the Scots translation makes for a very funny and original read – especially if it's read out loud!
■ *Angie Crawford, Bookseller at Waterstones*

IF YOU LIKE THIS, WHY NOT TRY . . .

THE GRUNTS IN TROUBLE
Philip Ardagh & Axel Scheffler

STINKBOMB AND KETCHUP-FACE AND THE GREAT BIG STORY NICKERS
John Dougherty & David Tazzyman

THE DAY THE CRAYONS QUIT
Drew Daywalt & Oliver Jeffers
(HarperCollins)

This very funny picture book tells the tale of a box of crayons who have had enough. Each colour writes a letter to their unfortunate owner Duncan, who's faced with a drawing dilemma as they threaten to strike unless things change. From arguments about what colour the sun is, to a favourite crayon who's worried he's going to wear out, each page is a hilarious homage to creativity.

There's lots of opportunity for discussion about what each crayon is used for and you'll need to put your imagination to good use to make sure no colours feel left out. Be inspired by Duncan and his pals and have a (fair and colour-balanced!) drawing session afterwards. Importantly, it's packed full of jokes and characters to entertain everyone again and again.

But be warned, you'll never look at a peach crayon the same way again . . .
■ *Sian Bevan, Performer, Writer & Producer*

IF YOU LIKE THIS, WHY NOT TRY . . .

	THERE ARE CATS IN THIS BOOK Viviane Schwarz
	ALL I SAID WAS Michael Morpurgo & Ross Collins

HORRID HENRY'S JUMBO JOKE BOOK
Francesca Simon & Tony Ross
(Orion)

What was the blackbird doing in the school library? Looking for bookworms. Get it?

Horrid Henry, the nation's favourite naughty boy, is famous for picking on Perfect Peter and getting into trouble with Miss Battle-Axe. He also has a talent for telling brilliant jokes. This jumbo three-books-in-one collection includes all of his best one-liners, doctor-doctor jokes, knock-knock gags and many more rib-ticklers.

Henry introduces some of the chapters himself but you don't need to know his books to enjoy his hilariously horrid jokes. There are whole sections dedicated to pongy pets, Santa and terrible teachers and the book comes with a 'too rude for parents' warning.

Indeed, this collection will give you loads of ammunition to truly annoy and amuse your family and is packed with fiendish illustrations by Tony Ross, the illustrator of David Walliams' *Gangsta Granny* and other books.
■ *Danny Scott, Author*

IF YOU LIKE THIS, WHY NOT TRY . . .

	DIRTY BERTIE - WORMS! Alan MacDonald & David Roberts
	OOR WULLIE'S BIG BUCKET OF LAUGHS JOKE BOOK Oor Wullie (and pals)

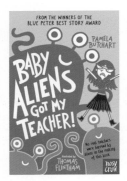

BABY ALIENS GOT MY TEACHER
Pamela Butchart & Thomas Flintham
(Nosy Crow)

Izzie and her friends are suspicious. Their teacher Miss Jones has changed for the better – or has she? Her nice behaviour is so out of character they suspect the worst . . . ALIENS!!! As they seem to be the only ones to have noticed their teacher's transformation, it must be their job to investigate before it's too late.

Told in the first person by Izzie in a rambling recount of the INCIDENT that led her to being sent to her room by her mum; we are treated to a fast-paced, accident-laden trail of near misses until eventually we find out what really happened to Miss Jones.

The writing style is easy to read and suitable for reading alone or to a class, one of my favourite pastimes. I enjoyed this book a lot and will be looking out for more work by Pamela Butchart.
■ *Gillian Caddy, Teaching Assistant*

IF YOU LIKE THIS, WHY NOT TRY . . .

 COMPLETELY CASSIDY, ACCIDENTAL GENIUS Tamsyn Murray

 THE TURBULENT TERM OF TYKE TILER Gene Kemp

DANGER IS EVERYWHERE: A HANDBOOK FOR AVOIDING DANGER
David O'Doherty & Chris Judge
(Penguin)

Everyone knows that the only safe way to get rid of a bee in your house is to dress as a queen bee and have it follow you out, but what do you do when a toothbrush snake goes up your nose? Or you think your Granny's been replaced by a robot? Or it SNOWS?!

In *Danger is Everywhere*, Docter Noel Zone (Docter's his first name. I am a good speller!) explains, among other things, PEBBs (Personal Emergency Bum Bags), T-CODs (Tiny Capes Of Dangerology) and LOFDing (Looking Out For Danger) while taking you through his TTTFADIES (Top Ten Tips For Avoiding Danger In Everyday Situations).

Thanks to this hilarious, brilliantly illustrated guide, you'll be well on your way to earning your Level One DOD (Diploma Of Dangerology). Just be ready for anything and be sure to watch out for the page nine scorpion!
■ *Fiona McDonald, Bookseller at Blackwell's*

IF YOU LIKE THIS, WHY NOT TRY . . .

 FORTUNATELY THE MILK Neil Gaiman & Chris Riddell

 WHY EATING BOGEYS IS GOOD FOR YOU Mitchell Symons

YOU TELL ME
Michael Rosen & Roger McGough
(Puffin)

Have you met PC Plod? Do you know what a 'nooligan' is? Have you ever wondered where broccoli comes from? Are you sure you want to know?

Welcome to the anarchic world of Michael Rosen and Roger McGough, playful poets who treat language like a football to be kicked around and bounced off walls. There's a wealth of rhythms and rhymes in these wickedly funny poems about childhood, school and bad habits.

Be warned: some are not for the faint-hearted. 'The Lesson', for example, comes with the disclaimer:

'Contains scenes of cartoon violence which some adults may find unsettling'. Some are utter nonsense. Why, for example, does Grandpa take his bucket for a walk? And some are downright gross. You probably DO NOT want to know where broccoli comes from. But there's no sense like nonsense. Who would have thought poetry could be so much fun?

■ *Neil Hepburn, Filmmaker & Marketing Manager at Cameo Cinema*

IF YOU LIKE THIS, WHY NOT TRY . . .

SUPER HAPPY MAGIC FOREST
Matty Long

PLEASE MRS BUTLER
Allan Ahlberg

DISGUSTING SCIENCE: A REVOLTING LOOK AT WHAT MAKES THINGS GROSS
Glenn Murphy
(Macmillan)

Why do we find some things absolutely revolting? *Disgusting Science* explores everything gross from bogies to bed bugs, dung beetles to flesh-eating parasites.

Why do we find some things disgusting and others not? Why do other people find the same things normal and sometimes even tasty? Foul foods, revolting animals, body fluids and disgusting diseases; with pages of hilariously fascinating facts and detailed descriptions of the most revolting aspects of life, the reasons behind

disgust are laid bare. Is it all to do with fear?

It's so disgustingly gross, I couldn't stop reading it and have been freaking out friends and family with these repulsive facts ever since. I'll never look at food and bodily excretions in the same way again. 'Eek! Get Away from Me!' Fantastic!

■ *Dr Gillian Lang, Deputy Director of Science at Glasgow Science Centre*

IF YOU LIKE THIS, WHY NOT TRY . . .

WHAT MAKES YOUR BODY WORK
Gill Arbuthnott

THE SILLY BOOK OF SIDE SPLITTING STUFF
Andy Seed & Scott Garrett

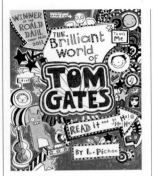

THE BRILLIANT WORLD OF TOM GATES
Liz Pichon
(Scholastic)

The hilarious Tom Gates series is well loved by children the whole world over – and it's not hard to see why. With jaw-achingly funny adventures, intricate doodles and a real-life diary feel, there is something for everyone in these books.

The Brilliant World of Tom Gates is basically a beginner's guide to Tom himself. You'll get to know about his favourite treats, teachers and, of course, his favourite band. This book follows Tom's extreme efforts to obtain tickets for his favourite band, Dude3, and his sister's efforts to stop him.

As a huge comic book fan myself, I love the style the Tom Gates series is written in. I think it's really accessible for everyone and I very much enjoyed trying to copy the doodles into my own notebook! With ten books in the series (and possibly more to come) it's a fantastic way to start your reading journey.
■ *Antonia Clark, Scottish Book Trust*

IF YOU LIKE THIS, WHY NOT TRY . . .

THE 13-STOREY TREEHOUSE
Andy Griffiths & Terry Denton

TIMMY FAILURE: MISTAKES WERE MADE
Stephan Pastis

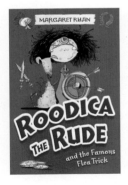

ROODICA THE RUDE AND THE FAMOUS FLEA TRICK
Margaret Ryan & Sarah Horne
(Catnip Publishing)

Set in Roman Britain, this is the first in a series of funny tales about Princess Roodica, the youngest daughter of the Celtic King of Brensland and Queen Goodica.

Roodica is a feisty heroine who fights back against the invading Romans along with her trusty companions, Fleabag the wolfhound, Plodette the pony and Gideon the horse boy. She is untidy, naughty and stubborn and not at all like her sisters, Foodica and Woodica, who are considered 'proper' princesses.

However, it's Roodica who's our real hero and she's the one who comes up with a cunning plan to retrieve a chair stolen by the local tax collector and his snotty son.

Will she succeed? Will she ever learn to drive a chariot safely? You'll have to read the book to find out and join her on her historic and terribly exciting adventures!
■ *Jacqueline Adam, Children's Librarian*

IF YOU LIKE THIS, WHY NOT TRY . . .

DARCY BUDDOCK: HI SO MUCH
Laura Dockrill

DORK DIARIES
Rachel Renee Russell

Folklore &
Fairytales

PETER PAN: THE GRAPHIC NOVEL
Stref & Fin Cramb
(Birlinn)

Peter Pan has been a childhood staple since JM Barrie's play was first performed in 1904. For many, it's the Disney animated film that has supplied the imagery which accompanies the story. I must confess that this film had such an effect on my young self that I insisted my parents call their imminent new child 'Wendy' if it was a girl. She was and they did.

This new graphic novel adaption of *Peter Pan* by Stref successfully supplants the comforting cartoon visuals of Walt Disney and returns the story to the darker mood and imagery of the early 20th century. The formal compositions and fastidious linework echo the stage presentations of the original drama while transporting the reader to an exotic and magical Neverland, where thrilling adventures await. Fully supporting the narrative, Fin Cramb's luminous colour work adds an atmospheric magic of its own.

My sister would love it, too.
■ *Dave Gibbons, Comic Writer, Artist & the first Comics Laureate*

IF YOU LIKE THIS, WHY NOT TRY . . .

 SPIDERWICK CHRONICLES - THE FIELD GUIDE
Tony DiTerlizzi & Holly Black

 OUTLAW: THE LEGEND OF ROBIN HOOD GRAPHIC
Tony Lee & Sam Hart

THE SECRET OF THE KELPIE
Lari Don & Philip Longson
(Floris Books)

One perfectly sunny day, playing by the shores of your typical breathtaking Scottish loch, Flora and her brothers and sisters are met by a seemingly tame and elegant white horse. Flora errs on the side of caution as her fun-seeking siblings clamber onto the creature's back, unknowingly sealing their fates. For this is no placidly mannered albeit beautiful horse; it's a kelpie (audible gasp), a dangerous water horse with a penchant for stealing children.

Get your hands on a copy to find out if the plucky young Flora is quick-witted enough to figure out the secret of the kelpie before all is lost.

Spun together from timeless myths and folklore by the award-winning genius mind of Lari Don, and paired with stunning I-want-to-step-right-into-them illustrations from Philip Longson, this is the latest edition of the Scottish Traditional Tales collection from Floris Books. A real treat for the eyes, no matter what age you are.
■ *Matthew Land, Illustrator & Bookseller at Blackwell's*

IF YOU LIKE THIS, WHY NOT TRY . . .

 AN ILLUSTRATED TREASURY OF SCOTTISH FOLK AND FAIRY TALES
Theresa Breslin & Kate Leiper

 THE MOST WONDERFUL THING IN THE WORLD
Viv French & Angela Barrett

WHO'S AFRAID OF THE BIG BAD BOOK?
Lauren Child
(Hachette)

Herb loves books, but books don't really love Herb. Instead of just reading them and looking at the pictures, he draws on character's faces, rips out pages and shoves them back in the wrong way. He even drops food on them.

Then something amazing happens, something we'd all secretly like to try – Herb falls inside his book. There he meets a screechy-voiced Goldilocks, a Queen with a drawn-on moustache, Cinderella missing her Prince Charming (Herb cut him out) and other well-loved characters Herb has mistreated.

The idea behind Lauren Child's book is so unusual, it's impossible not to get drawn into it. Although it's not just the words she's written that entertain, it's the way she's written them. Text drifts across the page in different fonts and sizes, while Herb's scribbles, food splodges and rips are scattered throughout – and, as with all Child's books, her wonderfully quirky illustrations bring the story to life.

■ *Kelly Apter, Arts Journalist*

IF YOU LIKE THIS, WHY NOT TRY . . .

	LITTLE RED HOOD Marjolaine Leray & Sarah Ardizzone
	HERE COME THE TROLLS Ron Butlin

THE GIRL WHO CIRCUMNAVIGATED FAIRYLAND IN A SHIP OF HER OWN MAKING
Catherynne M Valente &
Ana Juan
(Macmillan)

Take a trip to fairyland by sailing right on in to the fabulous fantasy world of Catherynne M Valente. Join 12-year-old September as she meets Green Wind (taking the form of a gentleman in a green jacket) and leaves her normal life behind.

Why does she go with this mysterious stranger? Because not only is her dad at war and her mum at work, it turns out Fairyland really, really needs her help. The Marquess who's in charge is unpredictable and fickle, and desperately in need of a special talisman – one that only September can fetch.

I've never read a book that made fairies sound as much fun as this one does. Fairyland is like nowhere you've ever been before but the best thing is that because this is the first book in the series, you'll have the chance to visit again and again.

■ *Martha MacDiarmid, Animation Producer*

IF YOU LIKE THIS, WHY NOT TRY . . .

	THE NEW POLICEMAN Kate Thompson
	CLAY David Almond

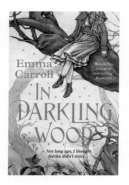

IN DARKLING WOOD
Emma Carroll
(Faber & Faber)

Alice is sent to live with her estranged grandmother at Darkling Cottage when her brother is admitted to hospital for a heart transplant. Her story is interwoven with letters from a young girl living in the cottage in 1918, nervously awaiting the return of her brother from WWI.

The girls' tales of hope and longing are tied into the story of the magic that lurks in the wood next to Darkling Cottage and the damage that may be done, and family secrets that may be revealed, by a plan to cut it down.

The book has all of the qualities of a classic that's been around for a very long time and is reminiscent of work by some of my favourite writers for children, such as Helen Cresswell, Joan Aitken and Sylvia Waugh.

Carroll seamlessly weaves reality with magic, making you wonder what enchantments might exist in our own everyday lives.
■ *Heather Collins, Scottish Book Trust*

IF YOU LIKE THIS, WHY NOT TRY . . .

	SHADOW FOREST Matt Haig
	LILLIPUT Sam Gayton

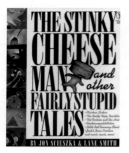

THE STINKY CHEESE MAN AND OTHER FAIRLY STUPID TALES
Jon Scieszka & Lane Smith
(Puffin)

Sometimes fairly stupid stories are the best ones. If you've read lots of fairytales and thought the characters were annoying, or the endings too happy, then this is the book for you. Find out what the Little Red Hen is actually like (super annoying), and what really happens when you kiss a frog.

This is a collection of super short stories, which can be read individually for a quick gulp of comedy, or slugged down whole as Jack the Narrator tries desperately to keep things in order.

Like a cheeky squirrel pulling the rug from under Cinderella, *The Stinky Cheese Man* is the opposite of that bit in a Disney film where all their wishes come true.

The illustrations are beautiful, and even the text layouts add to the fairly stupid nature of everything. Perfect for glum days when you need something a bit sarcastic to balance all the glittery fairytales out there.
■ *Sian Bevan, Performer, Writer & Producer*

IF YOU LIKE THIS, WHY NOT TRY . . .

	LOB Linda Newbery
	MR WOLF'S PANCAKES Jan Fearnley

BALACH NA BONAID
James Robertson & JoJo Norris (Translated by Aonghas MacNeacail)
(Big Sky Press)

Tha Niall a' fuireach còmhla ri sheanmhair agus an cat beag glas aca ann an taigh beag geal ri taobh na mara. Aon latha, an dèidh dha damh mòr eireachdail fhaicinn, tha Niall a' fàgail sàbhailteachd a' ghàrraidh air cuairt-dànachd dhan choille. Chan eil còir aig Niall a dhol faisg air a' choille dhorcha oir tha Ùruisg ann, a tha a sheanmhair air innse dha a dh'itheas gillean beaga son a dhìnnear!

Leugh mun chuairt-dànachd aig Niall tron choille agus mar a rinn e car a' mhuiltein, a' goirteachadh a chas agus a' dol air chall. Ciamar is urrainn dha a charaidean Niall a chuideachadh dhachaigh mus lorg an t-Ùruisg e? Chan eil fios aig duine dè an coltas a th' air Ùruisg le sin 's dòcha gum bi beagan eagal ort!

Leugh seo agus thèid thu fhèin air chall - chan ann idir an coille dhorcha far a bheil Ùruisg eagalach a' tàmh - ach ann an leabhar sgoinneil far a bheil dealbhan àlainn le Jojo Norris.

■ *Rosemary Ward, Director of the Comhairle nan Leabhraichean*

IF YOU LIKE THIS, WHY NOT TRY . . .

REALLY WEIRD REMOVALS.COM
Daniela Sacerdoti

WE'RE IN THE WRONG BOOK!
Richard Byrne

THE DRAGON STOORWORM
Theresa Breslin & Matthew Land
(Floris Books)

Princess Gemdelovely, the king's daughter, wants to choose the person she will marry – but first they have to free Scotland from the Dragon Stoorworm.

Dragon Stoorworm is the biggest dragon ever and it's eating whole herds of sheep, drinking dry most of the lochs and burning half of the crops with the flames that shoot out of its mouth! When Princess Gemdelovely and Assipattle meet and get to know each other, they decide to set off armed with the king's sword to get rid of the Dragon Stoorworm.

But can they do what many warriors before them have failed to do? Can this adventurous and courageous princess and her young man find a way to defeat such a fearsome dragon? And if they do what will happen to the dragon? Will Princess Gemdelovely and Assipattle live happily together in Scotland? Find out the answers in this beautifully illustrated and totally thrilling traditional Scottish folk tale.

■ *Helen Adair, Librarian*

IF YOU LIKE THIS, WHY NOT TRY . . .

FIRST AID FOR FAIRIES AND OTHER FABLED BEASTS
Lari Don

THE GLASS MOUNTAIN
Jan Pienkowski and David Walser

The New York Times Bestseller

A TALE DARK AND GRIMM
Adam Gidwitz
(Andersen Press)

Adam Gidwitz puts a modern spin on the familiar 'Once upon a time . . . ' in a series of new adventures with Hansel and Gretel at the helm.

If you think you've seen and heard it all when it comes to fairy tales, then this humorous take on the genre is just for you. Gidwitz splices together new stories in a traditional style with a modern narrative voice that adds some excellent comedic commentary and context.

Each chapter is a stand-alone story, making it easy to dip in and out of Hansel and Gretel's adventures.

Be warned though, these tales are not for the faint-hearted. These are stories with sacrifice, loss (of limb!) and inspiring lessons about dealing with how life can be scary and the fact that, yes, grown-ups can get things wrong sometimes.
■ *Eleanor Pender, Communications Executive at Edinburgh UNESCO City of Literature Trust*

IF YOU LIKE THIS, WHY NOT TRY . . .

THE SISTERS GRIMM: THE FAIRYTALE DETECTIVES
Michael Buckley

CLOCKWORK
Philip Pullman

MICHAEL MORPURGO
The Orchard Book of
Aesop's Fables
EMMA CHICHESTER CLARK

THE ORCHARD BOOK OF AESOP'S FABLES
Michael Morpurgo & Emma Chichester Clark
(Orchard)

Classic tales are given an up-to-date voice and lots of cheerful illustrations in this collaboration from former Children's Laureate Michael Morpurgo and award-winning illustrator Emma Chichester Clark.

In Aesop's world, animals pit their wits against one another, and humans learn the value of trust and honesty. Morpurgo's gentle peppering of modern language brings out the personality in his characters – lazy lions, wily foxes, arrogant rats, and shy mice come leaping off the page – while

Chichester Clark's bold colours and soft brushstrokes are simple and glorious. At the end of each tale, there's a summary of the moral, encouraging readers to be happy with what they have or to avoid crying wolf.

Whether you're reconnecting with Aesop's little moral gems or meeting them for the first time, this is a book packed with plenty of wonder and intrigue.
■ *Lucy Ribchester, Author & English Tutor*

IF YOU LIKE THIS, WHY NOT TRY . . .

FALLING OUT OF THE SKY: POEMS ABOUT MYTHS AND MONSTERS
Rachel Piercey & Emma Wright

THE HOUSE OF THE CATS: AND OTHER TALES FROM EUROPE
Maggie Pearson

Sport

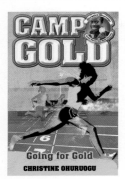

CAMP GOLD: GOING FOR GOLD
Christine Ohuruogu
(Tamarind)

Promising young track and field athlete Maxine Fula has earned a place at Camp Gold International in Spain. Once there she must prove herself against the world's top runners in her age group, under a blazing sun and the watchful eyes of her coaches.

It's a dream come true for Maxine but things start going wrong from day one. She is lagging behind her rivals in the 800 metres and is implicated in a spate of vandalism at the fancy campus. Can Maxine catch the vandals off the track and her rivals on it?

The second instalment of

Christine Ohuruogu's Camp Gold series is a fast-paced insight into the world of athletics and the sacrifices its competitors must make to get to the very top. As a former Olympic 400 metre champion, the author uses her real-life experience to create thrilling race scenes against a backdrop of crime and intrigue.
■ *Danny Scott, Author*

IF YOU LIKE THIS, WHY NOT TRY . . .

THE FASTEST BOY IN THE WORLD
Elizabeth Laird

HARRY MILLER'S RUN
David Almond

FLYING FERGUS: THE BEST BIRTHDAY BIKE
Chris Hoy, Joanna Nadin & Clare Elsom
(Picadilly Press)

Our young hero Fergus is ordinary in every way possible, apart from his brilliant imagination and a great love for bicycles. Living above Grandpa Herc's junk shop gives him the partnership and the means to build a bike and fight off bullies.

I can see a younger me in Fergus, and that's the magic of the story – enough characters we can all relate to and familiar places (especially if you know Edinburgh), but with the magic and mystery of a child's imagination, a

wonderful blurring of the real and the dream world.

'No one is a born champion' replied Grandpa, 'and it's not about luck.'

Here is a book that adults and children can enjoy, laced with experience and values, but most importantly, a brilliant story of adventure, ingenuity and creativeness.
■ *Mark Beaumont, Round the World Cyclist, Broadcaster & Author*

IF YOU LIKE THIS, WHY NOT TRY . . .

A HERO ON A BICYCLE
Shirley Hughes

HANK ZIPZER: THE WORLD'S GREATEST UNDERACHIEVER IS THE PING-PONG WIZARD
Henry Winkler & Lin Oliver

RUGBY ACADEMY: COMBAT ZONE
Tom Palmer
(Barrington Stoke)

Combat Zone is a realistic and captivating story set in a boarding school for children who have parents in the armed forces. Football-mad Woody is new at the school and all he wants to do is escape and find his fighter pilot dad – but he is too late because his dad has been sent to fight in the Middle East.

Woody is left worried and unhappy and, to top it all, the school don't play football – they play rugby! Will Woody have a go and use the sport to shake off his worries and become part of the school team?

This story feels very real – Woody adjusting to a new school, trying out a new sport, missing his dad – and you really find yourself willing him on to succeed and feel happier. It's not just about rugby either, as we learn more about the dangers Woody's dad faces at war.
■ *Cat Anderson, Bookseller at The Edinburgh Book Shop*

IF YOU LIKE THIS, WHY NOT TRY . . .

	RUGBY SPIRIT: A NEW SCHOOL, A NEW SPORT, AN OLD MYSTERY Gerard Siggins
	OLYMPIC POEMS Brian Moses & Roger Stevens

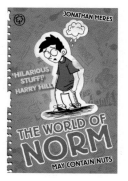

THE WORLD OF NORM: #1 MAY CONTAIN NUTS
Jonathan Meres
(Orchard)

Life isn't fair. Norm doesn't understand his family. His dad is currently out of work and stressed out and his Mum is obsessed with the shopping channels and constantly buys things that they don't need. He hates that they've moved to a new house and his younger brothers are just so annoying; like midges, no matter how much you swat them away, they always come back. All Norm dreams about is a new bike and becoming the youngest ever mountain biking champion. Life would be so much simpler if he had been raised in the Belgian rainforest by zebras.

The writing is witty and thought-provoking all the way through and, more than that, it's often laugh-out-loud funny. The start of the book when Norm, disorientated by the move mistakes his parents' bedroom for the bathroom, sets the light-hearted tone and, throughout all his trials, Norm still has his dreams of being a World Champion.
■ *Julia Williams, School Librarian*

IF YOU LIKE THIS, WHY NOT TRY . . .

	SCOTLAND STARS FC: CALUM'S NEW TEAM Danny Scott
	DIARY OF A TENNIS PRODIGY Shamini Flint & Sally Heinrich

DAISY AND THE TROUBLE WITH SPORTS DAY
Kes Gray & Nick Sharratt
(Red Fox)

This is one instalment in the series that charts the many trials and troubles of Daisy as she negotiates her sometimes difficult, confusing and bizarre journey through school.

Daisy has never been a very big fan of sports day. From loud whistles to throwing things made of foam and having to pronounce the names of pastas, there's lots about it that troubles her, but after her friend Gabby is injured, Daisy attempts to overcome her problems and win the race for her best friend.

The interactivity of the series is what really makes Daisy jump from the page. From fun illustrations and cool codes that link to a trouble index listing every obstacle in Daisy's way, to a sports day quiz designed to test your memory, the pages are full of imaginative ways to tune into Daisy's unique way of viewing the world.
■ *Nicola Brown, Teacher*

IF YOU LIKE THIS, WHY NOT TRY . . .

FLAMING OLYMPICS
Michael Coleman, Mike Phillips & Adian Potts

VULGAR THE VIKING AND THE GREAT GULP GAMES
Odin Redbeard

LOLLIPOP AND GRANDPA GO SWIMMING
Penelope Harper & Cate James
(Phoenix Yard Books)

When you can't swim, the swimming pool can seem like a huge scary place. And when Lollipop is confronted with the local pool, she just wants to sneak away home. But thank goodness Grandpa is with her. This picture book can help you see that you can do anything with the right encouragement. Grandpa offers reassuring words, a hand to hold and a fantastic imagination, which all help Lollipop take those first steps and breaths and kicks in the water.

It's hard to take your eyes off the smashing, splashy illustrations. Eagle-eyed readers will enjoy looking at all the swimmers in the ENORMOUS pool, and spotting the giant octopus, the big blue whale and the pirates before Lollipop and Grandpa meet them face-to-face. This beautiful book is sure to make even the most reluctant swimmer look at swimming pools in a whole new way.
■ *Emma Andrew, Teacher*

IF YOU LIKE THIS, WHY NOT TRY . . .

IN AT THE DEEP END
Michelle Magorian

THE TAIL OF EMILY WINDSNAP
Liz Kessler

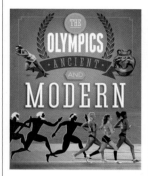

THE OLYMPICS: ANCIENT TO MODERN: A GUIDE TO THE HISTORY OF THE GAMES
Joe Fullman
(Wayland)

Discover everything you could want to know about the world's greatest sporting event, all in one handy book! Covering the history of the games from ancient Greece right up to the modern day, this bright and beautifully designed book is jam-packed with fascinating facts about the Olympics. Celebrate with the winners and commiserate with the losers as you delve into all of the biggest questions about the games. Who are the fastest, strongest and most skilled athletes the world has ever seen? Which cities have hosted the event? What happened when there was trouble at the Olympic Games? What's the difference between the Winter and Summer Games? Who has won the most medals? Learn all of the answers – and plenty more fun facts beside – in this bumper book of Olympic insights.
■ *Catriona Wallace, Scottish Book Trust*

IF YOU LIKE THIS, WHY NOT TRY . . .

	TOP OF THE LEAGUE Andrea Mills & Clive Gifford
	A HORRID FACTBOOK: HORRID HENRY SPORTS Francesca Simon & Tony Ross

CHARLIE MERRICK'S MISFITS IN FOULS, FRIENDS AND FOOTBALL
Dave Cousins
(OUP)

Charlie Merrick knows that it's going to be difficult for his under-12s team, North Star Galaxy, to stay out of the relegation zone this year, and he's ready to do anything and everything to see his gang of 'misfits' succeed.

As the season goes on, it seems like Charlie's plan might just be working. But at what cost? As friendships suffer and feelings get hurt, Charlie has to do some hard thinking – maybe there's something more important than winning after all?

Writer and illustrator Dave Cousins tells this gripping story of success against the odds using match reports, tactical diagrams, comics and more, so every turn of the page brings something new and unexpected. The book is a great read for football fans, but you don't need to be sporty to get wrapped up in the action on and off the pitch with these quirky characters.
■ *Jo Caird, Freelance Travel & Arts Journalist*

IF YOU LIKE THIS, WHY NOT TRY . . .

	THE BARE BUM GANG AND THE FOOTBALL FACE-OFF Anthony McGowan
	EXTRA TIME Morris Gleitzman

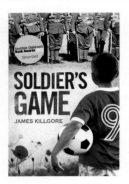

SOLDIER'S GAME
James Killgore
(Kelpies)

Have you ever received a family heirloom and wondered about the person who first owned it?

That's exactly what happens to Ross when his grandmother hands over her father's precious box. In it, he finds an old pair of football boots, a Heart of Midlothian football strip and a photograph of Jack, Ross's great-grandfather.

Alternating between present day Edinburgh where Ross and his teammates are suffering an abysmal season as Bruntsfield Primary's P7 football team, and the early months of WWI, Soldier's Game tells the story of the formation and early days of the Royal Scots 16th Battalion, also known as the Hearts Battalion. It gives us a sense of life in 1914 Edinburgh and the popular attitudes to war at that time using historical fact and fictional characters.

This book should appeal to anyone with an interest in the glorious game and especially 'Jambo' fans everywhere, or anyone who loves to soak up our history and heritage.
■ *Linda Murray, Teacher*

IF YOU LIKE THIS, WHY NOT TRY . . .

 FRIENDLY MATCHES
Allan Ahlberg, Janet Ahlberg & Fritz Wegner

 THE CHRISTMAS TRUCE
Carol Ann Duffy & David Roberts

THE ANTI-PRINCESS CLUB: BELLA'S BACKYARD BULLIES
Samantha Turnbull & Sarah Davies
(Allen & Unwin)

While there's plenty of excitement and adventure in Samantha Turnbull's story, perhaps the most important thing she gives us is four strong female role models. From their treehouse base, Bella, Chloe, Emily and Grace set about righting wrongs, fulfilling their ambitions and even changing the world a little bit.

The second in Turnbull and Davies' Anti-Princess Club series finds the girls targeted by a cyberbully, who warns them to 'watch your back'. Computer whizz Emily digs deep inside their club website, footballer Grace teaches the girls to tackle boys on the pitch, scientist Chloe finds a comet in the sky, and designer Bella creates a planetarium to view it by. So no shortage of inspirational young women who, in their own words, 'don't need rescuing'. It's also an intriguing read, as we discover who's behind the nastiness – and why.
■ *Kelly Apter, Arts Journalist*

IF YOU LIKE THIS, WHY NOT TRY . . .

 FOOTBALL JOKES: FANTASTICALLY FUNNY JOKES FOR FOOTBALL FANATICS

 SWAN: THE LIFE AND DANCE OF ANNA PAVLOVA
Laura Snyder & Julie Morstad

History

THE THIEVES OF OSTIA
Caroline Lawrence
(Orion)

This is the first book in the Roman Mysteries series, and introduces you to Flavia Gemina, a Roman girl living in the port of Ostia, her Jewish neighbour Jonathan, a beggar boy called Lupus and a slave girl, Nubia. It starts with a brilliant first chapter, in which Flavia solves a mystery using intelligence and observation, then gets herself into danger when she tries to prove she's right . . .

The four new friends meet while solving a bigger mystery – who is beheading local dogs and why – and their first adventure has a few dark moments. But *The Thieves Of Ostia* sets up this wonderful series in a fun and exciting way, with a pack of feral dogs, a chase by slavers, and a mysterious thief in the night.

I enjoyed learning surprising details of Roman life in the company of four memorable characters. And everyone loves solving a mystery!
■ *Lari Don, Writer*

IF YOU LIKE THIS, WHY NOT TRY . . .

JULIUS ZEBRA: BUNDLE WITH THE BRITONS
Gary Northfield

ROMANS ON THE RAMPAGE
Jeremy Strong

ASTERIX AND THE PECHTS (ASTERIX AND THE PICTS IN SCOTS)
Rene Goscinny, Albert Uderzo, Jean-Yves Ferri & Didier Conrad (translated by Matthew Fitt)
(Itchy Coo)

I've always loved Asterix and his giant pal Obelix, who're always using their wit, nouse and maybe a little magic potion to hold out against the Roman invasion from their wee village in ancient Gaul.

This first Asterix volume from a new creative team, Jean-Yves Ferri and Didier Conrad, has been lovingly translated into Scots by Matthew Fitt and sees our heroes travelling from France to the kingdom of Scotland.

Some of my earliest understanding of puns and wordplay jokes came from finding them in Asterix books. There was always joy in the humour and this Scots-translated story is one of the best. It's full of the usual brilliant rammies and misadventures and Fitt has a lot of fun with the translation, adapting every joke to fit and even employing different local Scots dialects for different characters!
■ *Fin Cramb, Comic Writer & Artist*

IF YOU LIKE THIS, WHY NOT TRY . . .

DRAGONS AT CRUMBLING CASTLE
Terry Pratchett

ROMAN SOLDIER'S HANDBOOK
Lesley Sim & Ian McNee

THE PRINCE WHO WALKED WITH LIONS
Elizabeth Laird
(Macmillan)

Discover the story of the childhood of Prince Alamayu of Abyssinia, a real person who lived at the time of Queen Victoria.

Alamayu's comfortable life changes totally when the British army defeats his father and it is decided that he must go to Britain and learn how to be an English gentleman. Our hero has to travel far away without his family and servants and learn how to survive in a very different country. He's faced with ignorance and bullying from adults and other children but also makes many friends, including Queen Victoria herself!

This is a great story about someone who has to be very brave and rely on their skills to overcome many obstacles. It can be sad at times but also very dramatic as Alamayu survives a terrifying battle and later has to fight for respect in a strange new country.
■ *Paul Hudson, Librarian*

IF YOU LIKE THIS, WHY NOT TRY . . .

 THE HOUSE ON HUMMINGBIRD ISLAND
Sam Angus

 WHEN THE RAIN COMES
Tom Pow & Malika Favre

MARY QUEEN OF SCOTS AND ALL THAT
Alan Burnett & Scoular Anderson
(Birlinn)

Mary's life was a series of plots, intrigues, mysteries and twists. She became the Queen of Scotland at a very young age when her father, the King, died – but that was just the start of her troubles.

Young readers are given puzzles to try to solve in this telling of her story – how could Mary get the better of her long-time adversary John Knox? Who murdered her second husband Lord Darnley? Did her cousin and rival Queen Elizabeth have anything to do with it? How could she keep her baby son safe from kidnappers? How could she fulfill her mother's ambition? It was one difficult decision after another!

Mary's fascinating tale is told in a fun and engaging way, making the history come to life for children and drawing them in by asking them to try to work out possible solutions for her problems.
■ *Jenni Hamilton, Librarian*

IF YOU LIKE THIS, WHY NOT TRY . . .

 THE HILL OF THE RED FOX
Allan Campbell McLean

 PYRATE'S BOY
EB Colin

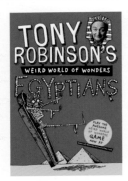

TONY ROBINSON'S WEIRD WORLD OF WONDERS: EGYPTIANS
Sir Tony Robinson
(Macmillan)

Join Tony and the Curiosity Crew on a journey through ancient Egypt, discovering some of the strangest, funniest, and most curious facts!

Did you know that one block from a pyramid weighs the same as a humpback whale? Or that ancient Egyptians ate mice cooked in oil as a cure for grey hair? Discover loads of facts and stories about fascinating mummies, strange-looking gods and fighting Egyptians in this fun non-fiction book. The Curiosity Crew bring the stories to life by appearing on every page with lots of photographs, cartoons and drawings.

I loved discovering more about the ancient Egyptians and really enjoyed that this book had lots of amazing facts that I didn't know. I even learned an Egyptian joke! Since reading it, I've looked at our ancient Egyptian objects in the museum differently – now I know some of their secrets!
■ *Sarah Cowie, Learning Officer (Schools) at National Museums Scotland*

IF YOU LIKE THIS, WHY NOT TRY . . .

 ANCIENT EGYPT: TALES OF GODS AND PHARAOHS Marcia Williams

 THE ADVENTURES O TINTIN: THE MERK O THE PHARAOH Herge (translated by Susan Rennie)

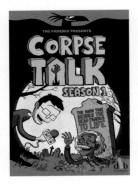

CORPSE TALK: SEASON ONE
Adam Murphy
(David Fickling Books)

Corpse Talk is a history book with a gruesome difference. Join host Adam Murphy as he interviews some of the biggest names in history, straight from the graveyard!

Ever wondered what killed Tutankhamun? Why Marie Antoinette lost her head? What inspired Charles Dickens? Or why Henry VIII had so many wives? Well, in *Corpse Talk*, Adam Murphy digs up the answers as he speaks to scientists, pioneering women, artists, inventors, writers, pirates, musicians and statesmen about their lives.

This book is definitely not for the faint-hearted; its illustrations are gruesome and gory. But, if you like history, comics, bad jokes, shock endings, mysteries and the downright weird, this is definitely the book for you.

And if you think you know your Einstein from your Curie, or your Churchill from your Wallace, you can take part in the body count challenge at the end of each section . . . if you dare!
■ *Lauren Throw, School Librarian*

IF YOU LIKE THIS, WHY NOT TRY . . .

 THE SIGN OF THE BLACK DAGGER Joan Lingard

 BARNABY GRIMES AND THE CURSE OF THE NIGHT WOLF Chris Riddell & Paul Stewart

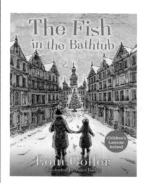

THE FISH IN THE BATHTUB
Eoin Colfer & Peter Bailey
(Barrington Stoke)

Set in 70s Poland, *A Fish in the Bathtub* is the moving story of Lucja and her rebellious grandfather Feliks. After years of oppression under Hitler and Stalin, Feliks has decided to have a traditional carp dinner for Christmas and buys a live fish on the black market. But Lucja falls in love with the carp as it awaits its fate in the bathtub.

The book weaves Lucja's developing fondness for the fish into Feliks' memories of the war, mixing serious moments of reflection with light-hearted playfulness. The story is bursting with ideas to explore with parents or grandparents, relationships to discuss and history to discover. Lucja's strong will and sense of injustice makes her someone to root for, and the moral of the story – self sacrifice as love – may move a few readers to tears.

The lovely detailed illustrations, short chapters and chunky fonts make it a very satisfying read.
■ *Marion Bourbouze, Director at Imaginate*

IF YOU LIKE THIS, WHY NOT TRY . . .	
	OPAL PLUMSTEAD Jacqueline Wilson
	WHEN HITLER STOLE PINK RABBIT Judith Kerr

ONCE
Morris Gleitzman
(Puffin)

When Felix finds a whole carrot in his soup one day at the orphanage (instead of specks of cabbage, rat poo or ceiling plaster), you know his life is never going to be the same again. Set in Nazi-occupied Poland, *Once* follows a young Jewish boy in his desperate attempt to find his parents who were booksellers before the Second World War. Felix loves to tell stories and his vivid imagination often gets him out of a tight spot – whether cheering up the other orphans he meets along the way or helping a Nazi officer who has toothache.

You know how when you read a book and it's sad, amazing, and funny all at the same time and you don't know whether to laugh or cry or both? That's *Once*. It is the first in a series of five books following Felix's story as he tries to evade capture by the Nazis with both hilarious and heartbreaking results.
■ *Emma Dunn, Scottish Book Trust*

IF YOU LIKE THIS, WHY NOT TRY . . .	
	FIVE CHILDREN ON THE WESTERN FRONT Kate Saunders
	WHAT ARE WE FIGHTING FOR? Brian Moses & Roger Stevens

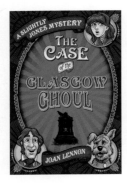

A SLIGHTLY JONES MYSTERY: THE CASE OF THE GLASGOW GHOUL
Joan Lennon
(Catnip Books)

In Victorian era Great Britain, aspiring detective and Sherlock Holmes super-fan, Slightly Jones, has only one objective in mind – to be as great as the famous detective himself!

When thieves target Glasgow's Hunterian museum and priceless artefacts seem to disappear into thin air, amateur sleuth Slightly is soon hot on the trail. As the mystery deepens, the suspects are as strange as the conundrum itself, including a one-legged man and his trained ape. Even a haunted graveyard falls under Slightly's watchful eye.

The book is teeming with a real sense of the period, creating a wonderful (although sometimes macabre) depiction of the harsh climate of the Victorian era, while still capturing the joy of discovery and invention that was so celebrated at the time. Sometimes bleak but constantly enthralling, this is a real page-turner and a great choice for aspiring sleuths.
■ *Nicola Brown, Teacher*

IF YOU LIKE THIS, WHY NOT TRY . . .

 THE ELEVENTH ORPHAN
Joan Lingard

 STREET CHILD
Berlie Doherty

STARS SHALL BE BRIGHT
Cathy MacPhail & Ollie Cuthbertson
(Barrington Stoke)

When their mother dies during the First World War, young James, William and Belle are left at the mercy of Mrs Carter, a downstairs neighbour. She's managed to persuade the whole street that she's a good Samaritan and nice person, but the children soon find out that she is really not what she seems. When Mrs Carter starts saying she might put the children into a home, James decides that they'd be better off fending for themselves. Instead of sitting around and hoping for the best, the children set off by train in search of their father, a soldier who has been fighting at the front.

The book is based around the true story of Scotland's worst train disaster and helps to paint a very vivid picture of what life might have been like during wartime. Join James and his siblings as they try to take their fate into their own hands.
■ *Neil Hamilton, Graphic Designer & Guide at Roslin Chapel*

IF YOU LIKE THIS, WHY NOT TRY . . .

 SCOTTISH TALES OF ADVENTURE: WORLD WAR I
Allan Burnett

 STAY WHERE YOU ARE AND THEN LEAVE
John Boyne

Magic &
Mystery

THE DREAMSNATCHER
Abi Elphinstone
(Simon & Schuster)

Thrill-seekers will love reading about Moll Pecksniff, who lives in a forest gypsy camp. Tormented by nightmares, she wakes from a vivid dream to find she has sleepwalked to the river boundary. Camp leader Oak has warned her never to cross to the Deepwood side, for witchdoctor Skull lives there.

But Skull's men have stolen Moll's beloved horse, so she crosses the river, armed with her trusty catapult and with wildcat Gryff following. When she sees the masked witchdoctor and hears his drums and rattles, she realises he has used dreams to lure her there. The Oracle Stones say: a child and a beast will come to fight the Dreamsnatcher. As Moll's destiny is revealed, Skull sets out to kill her. Can Moll and Gryff really stop him or will his dark magic prove too strong?

This is a fast-paced thriller with a powerful new heroine, and there's more! Follow Moll's next breathless adventure in *The Shadow Keeper*.
■ *Lindsay McKrell, Writer & Children's Librarian*

IF YOU LIKE THIS, WHY NOT TRY . . .

THE UNLIKELY ADVENTURES OF MABEL JONES
Will Mabbitt & Ross Collins

ONE WISH
Michelle Harrison

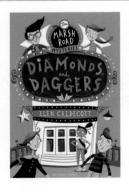

THE MARSH ROAD MYSTERIES: DIAMONDS AND DAGGERS
Elen Caldecott
(Bloomsbury)

This is the first in a series of books about a group of friends – Piotr, Minnie, Andrew, Flora and Sylvia – who solve mysteries. In this first book, Piotr's dad (a theatre security guard) is accused of stealing a big star's diamond necklace, and Piotr is told that the family will have to go back to Poland.

With his friends to help him, Piotr sets out to find the real diamond thief. There are lots of false leads and stake-outs which put the friends in peril. There are also plenty of clues, so you can try to figure out who the thief is at the same time as the gang.

I liked that there was a lot about the theatre and how it works, but my favourite thing about this book were the friends who were all really fun, and real – the sort of friends I'd like to have if I was in a fix!
■ *Cat Anderson, Bookseller at The Edinburgh Book Shop*

IF YOU LIKE THIS, WHY NOT TRY . . .

TWELVE MINUTES TO MIDNIGHT
Christopher Edge

MARIELLA MYSTERY INVESTIGATES: THE GHOSTLY GUINEA PIG
Kate Pankhurst

THE FAMOUS FIVE
Enid Blyton
(Hachette)

Meet the young crime-solving team that's always at the centre of the action in the very first book in the Famous Five series.

Julian, Dick, Anne, tomboy George and Timmy, her lovable dog, quickly get mixed up in solving the mystery of an old shipwreck off Kirrin Island. But they're not the only ones trying to find the treasure. The team has to do some super-sleuthing to save the gold – and George's island.

As the first set of 'grown-up' books I ever discovered I could read on my own, the Famous Five have a very special place in my heart.

I still remember running through to my parents' room to tell them I could read well enough to go adventuring with the Five without their help. And with 21 books in the series, I had plenty of escapades to look forward to!
■ *Lynsey May, Writer & Copywriter*

IF YOU LIKE THIS, WHY NOT TRY . . .

	SCHOOL SHIP TOBERMORY Alexander McCall Smith
	ADVENTURE ISLAND: THE MYSTERY OF THE WHISTLING CAVES Helen Moss

INKHEART
Cornelia Funke
(Chicken House)

Getting lost in a great story is the very best reason to read, but imagine if that happened literally. Imagine if the book you're reading came to life. It's every fervent reader's biggest wish. But as with all the best fables and fairy tales: careful what you wish for . . .

In *Inkheart*, Meggie and her father Mo live in an isolated but never lonely cottage, because it's overflowing with books. Mo is uniquely gifted and, several years ago, when reading from one book in particular, he read the characters into life. Dustfinger wants to return to the world of the story, but sinister

Capricorn wants Mo to use his powers for malevolent reasons. Can Meggie help her father?

Inkheart feels contemporary and classic all at once, full of fantastical adventure and affecting characters. It's also a book that celebrates books, stuffed with literary treasures, so obviously written by a book-lover for book-lovers.
■ *Keith Gray, Writer*

IF YOU LIKE THIS, WHY NOT TRY . . .

	ARCHIE GREEN AND THE MAGICIAN'S SECRET DD Everest
	THE BLACK BOOK OF SECRETS FE Higgins

THE MYSTERIES OF RAVENSTORM ISLAND: THE LOST CHILDREN
Gillian Philip
(Orchard)

A strange island packed with eerie statues, ominous warnings and enough secrets to mystify even the most curious mind; not what Molly expected when she travelled by seaplane to begin her summer at Ravenstorm Hall.

When her brother Jack disappears, she and her cousin Arthur (an unlikely duo) are compelled to join forces to save him. Against a backdrop of enveloping mists and scary silhouettes, they embark upon a quest to uncover the island's mystery. Do they have what it takes to solve the best kind of puzzle, the magical kind?

Perfect for a brave and curious spirit with an uninhibited imagination, this is a fast-paced adventure brimming with intrigue and magic! Like everything I loved to read growing up, I was entangled in the plot twists and reaching for the next in the series before I knew it. It's a real gem of a book.
■ *Jen Harwood, Scottish Book Trust*

IF YOU LIKE THIS, WHY NOT TRY . . .

 SOMETHING WICKEDLY WEIRD: THE WEREWOLF AND THE IBIS
Chris Mould

 BREE MCCREADY AND THE HALF-HEART LOCKET
Hazel Allan

THE ACCIDENTAL TIME TRAVELLER
Janis Mackay
(Kelpies)

FACT: a packet of Jaffa Cakes can change your life.

When Robbie's mum sends him to the shop for a packet of biscuits, a chance encounter with Agatha Black changes his life forever. At first, Robbie thinks Agatha is a bit crazy. She wears funny clothes, is scared of cars and talks funny. But it's when Robbie discovers that she's actually from 1812 that his life starts to get really complicated.

Can Robbie trust the rest of his gang with his secret? Can he solve the mystery of time travel and get Agatha back to her family for Christmas? Can he win the history prize and get the best bike ever? And can he do all this before Crow, the school bully, finds out Agatha's secret?

The Accidental Time Traveller is a race against time full of history, adventure, mystery and just a little bit of magic.
■ *Lauren Throw, School Librarian*

IF YOU LIKE THIS, WHY NOT TRY . . .

 TOM'S MIDNIGHT GARDEN
Philippa Pearce

 WHEN YOU REACH ME
Rebecca Stead

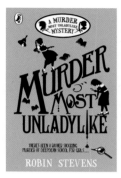

MURDER MOST UNLADYLIKE
Robin Stevens
(Penguin)

Deepdean School for Girls can be a very boring place and even after best friends Daisy Wells and Hazel Wong start their very own detective club, they still can't find anything that piques their interest. That all changes when they discover the body of their science teacher, which vanishes before they can show the authorities – and the girls soon realise their lives will never be boring again!

A loving and well-crafted callback to the boarding school mystery stories of the 1930s, *Murder Most Unladylike* updates the genre with a modern, darker edge to the crime. Our complex and smart heroines are also a lot more interesting than the ones you might find in more traditional stories.

A mix of Agatha Christie and Enid Blyton, Robin Stevens paints a vivid picture of school life in 1934, creating a riveting thriller with a real sense of romping adventure, in the mould of the Famous Five.

■ *Sean Watson, Comic Writer & Animator*

IF YOU LIKE THIS, WHY NOT TRY . . .	
	THE SCANDALOUS SISTERHOOD OF PRICKWILLOW PLACE Julie Berry
	THE MYSTERY OF THE CLOCKWORK SPARROW Katherine Woodfine

WITCH WARS
Sibeal Pounder & Laura Ellen Anderson
(Bloomsbury)

'For as long as anyone can remember, witches have lurked on this planet,' begins the first chapter in writer Sibeal Pounder and artist Laura Ellen Anderson's Witch Wars series. 'Most people think witches are really evil, but that's mostly nonsense and really only half the story.'

It's a story that young Tiga Whicabim comes to learn only too well, especially when she's rescued from a life being locked in a shed and fed cheese water by her awful guardian, Miss Heks. Spirited away down the plughole to the land of Sinkville by Fran the Fabulous Fairy (a name Fran made up for herself), Tiga is told she's really a witch. It's her turn to compete in Witch Wars, a contest to find the best witch.

Laura Ellen Anderson's illustrations give a strong sense of the incredible new world Tiga has found and *Witch Wars* is a fast and exciting read that's as funny as it is filled with great characters.

■ *David Pollock, Arts Journalist*

IF YOU LIKE THIS, WHY NOT TRY . . .	
	THE WORST WITCH Jill Murphy
	MAGICALAMITY Kate Saunders

HARRY POTTER AND THE PHILOSOPHER'S STONE
JK Rowling
(Bloomsbury)

Harry Potter is a regular 11-year-old boy, living with his aunt and uncle and trying to be as ordinary as possible, when mysterious letters begin arriving at his house. Once Harry learns he is really a wizard, his world is turned upside down as he begins his education at Hogwarts School of Witchcraft and Wizardry. *Harry Potter and the Philosopher's Stone* sees Harry, and his new friends Ron and Hermione, through their first year at Hogwarts, with all the excitement and adventure they find along the way.

Now a worldwide phenomenon, these books will always have a huge place in my heart. As a child who grew up with Harry Potter, I spent many nights camped outside my local bookshop awaiting the latest Harry Potter book. Luckily, all seven books have now been published, so you don't have to wait years to find out what happens next.
■ *Sasha de Buyl, Scottish Book Trust*

IF YOU LIKE THIS, WHY NOT TRY . . .

ALFIE BLOOM AND THE SECRETS OF HEXBRIDGE CASTLE
Gabrielle Kent

CHARMED LIFE
Diana Wynne Jones

WITCH BABY AND ME
Debi Gliori
(Random House)

Witch Baby and Me is the first in a hilarious series of illustrated chapter books exploring the adventures of nine-year-old Lily and her baby sister Daisy, who also happens to be a witch.

Only Lily knows the truth about Daisy's powers, and to make her life even more complicated, her mum has decided that they are all going to start a new life in the far north of Scotland.

The brilliantly plotted story follows their attempts to invite their decidedly odd neighbours to a house-warming party. The question is, will Daisy and her chaotic magic be a help or a hindrance? Children who enjoy quirky, fun tales with a good, strong dose of toilet humour will love this book – the narrative is easy to follow, with many laugh-out-loud moments, and Gliori's trademark illustrations match the story perfectly, bringing her bonkers characters vividly to life.
■ *Helen Croney, Scottish Book Trust*

IF YOU LIKE THIS, WHY NOT TRY . . .

THE DRAGON SITTER
Josh Lacey

THE OGRE OF OGLEFORT
Eva Ibbotson & Alex T Smith

Friendship
& Family

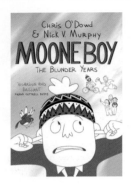

MOONE BOY
Chris O'Dowd & Nick V. Murphy
(Macmillan)

For 11-year-old Martin Moone, living in a family of girls is hard, but living with his imaginary friends is nearly impossible!

Outnumbered by his sisters, Martin attempts to rebalance the gender divide in the Moone household after his best friend Padraic tells him of a special catalogue where he can order his very own imaginary best friend. Martin's first choice, the aptly named Loopy Lou, is too wacky and only serves to annoy Martin further until he finds the more relaxed office clerk, Sean 'Caution' Murphy, who quickly becomes Martin's new wingman and guide.

Written as a prequel to the hit TV series, it's easy to see that many of the stories are based on things that really happened to the writer when he was growing up. A genuine warmth shines through the characters and world he has created, making *Moone Boy* a story that both kids and adults will love!
■ *Sean Watson, Comic Writer & Animator*

IF YOU LIKE THIS, WHY NOT TRY . . .

IMAGINARY FRED
Eoin Colfer & Oliver Jeffers

CLARICE BEAN, UTTERLY ME
Lauren Child

COSMIC
Frank Cottrell Boyce & Steven Lenton
(Macmillan)

Cosmic tells the story of Liam Digby, an extremely tall, computer game-obsessed 12-year-old who is frustrated at not being able to do all the things grown-ups can do.

Moving to a new school, he struggles to fit in with his classmates and strikes up an unlikely alliance with celeb-obsessed Florida Kirby at his local theatre group. Then Liam enters them both in a competition that leads to an out-of-this-world adventure!

Cosmic is a heart-warming adventure that zooms from an English school to a theme park in China and even out into space. It's a really funny read and the book is all about growing up, getting into trouble and the distance between parents and kids. I have really fond memories of reading *Cosmic* when my wife was pregnant with my son Rory. I'm looking forward to reading my copy with him.
■ *Colm Linnane, Librarian*

IF YOU LIKE THIS, WHY NOT TRY . . .

100 THINGS TO KNOW ABOUT SPACE
Alex Frith, Jerome Martin, Alice James, Federico Mariani & Shaw Neilsen

ALIENS STINK
Steve Cole

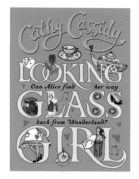

LOOKING GLASS GIRL
Cathy Cassidy
(Penguin)

Alice and her best friends are drifting apart. Not only that, but they also seem determined to make her life miserable, all under the guidance of the pretty, poised and perfect Savannah Hunter. A surprise invite to a sleepover at Savvy's house seems like it might change everything. And it does, only not in the way anyone would have wanted.

In this quirky reimagining of Lewis Carroll's classic tale, our unconscious Alice picks her way back through boys, friendship cliques and loneliness in an attempt to work out how she ended up caught halfway between the real world and a sinister Wonderland. And whether she fell down the rabbit hole, or if she was pushed. With an interesting narrative style and imaginative use of Carroll's themes and characters, this story will take you through the daunting transition between primary school and secondary, navigating that tricky terrain between being a kid and becoming a teenager.
■ *Candice Purwin, Illustrator & Comic Writer*

IF YOU LIKE THIS, WHY NOT TRY . . .	
	SCARLETT AND IVY - THE LOST TWIN Sophie Cleverly
	THE BOY IN THE BISCUIT TIN Heather Dyer

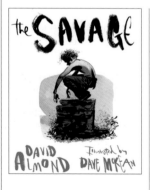

THE SAVAGE
David Almond & Dave McKean
(Walker)

For Blue, a young boy trying to come to terms with a death in the family, solace comes from his wild imaginings of a feral, savage figure living in the nearby woods. But as with all wild things, Blue begins to worry that the Savage isn't staying where he should . . .

A stunning and unusual prose and graphic novel hybrid, *The Savage* has a unique voice all of its own. Sometimes the words are the focus and sometimes the images take centre stage, and it's genuinely a joy to read.

I've always felt that the best children's stories don't hide from a kind of darkness and honesty that we all encounter growing up, and *The Savage* runs brave and barefoot through that territory beautifully.

Almond and McKean are masters of sparse and deft description, perfectly capturing both stillness and raw emotion – all with a quiet hum of magic in the background.
■ *Fin Cramb, Comic Writer & Artist*

IF YOU LIKE THIS, WHY NOT TRY . . .	
	THE ARRIVAL Shaun Tan
	DANNY CHAMPION OF THE WORLD Roald Dahl

THE RUNNER
Keith Gray
(Random House)

'It wasn't running away . . . Not really'. Jason's mum and dad are always fighting and he misses his big brother, Michael, who has moved to Liverpool. Fed up with everything, Jason decides that he will take the Intercity train and go visit his brother and just escape his life for a little while.

On board the train, Jason meets Jam. Jam is a runner. He and other runners live on board the Intercity trains, hiding in the toilets, stealing food from the buffet and sleeping on the overhead luggage racks when the trains are out of use. Jason is intrigued by all these lost boys, secretly living in constant transit.

Set over the course of the train trip, this is Jason's journey to understanding his parents and himself. *The Runner* is a short novel, packed with a strong sense of adventure and a brilliant twist in the tale!
■ *Janet Smyth, Children & Education Programme Director at Edinburgh International Book Festival*

IF YOU LIKE THIS, WHY NOT TRY . . .	
	LIAR AND SPY Rebecca Stead
	CTRL-Z Andrew Norriss

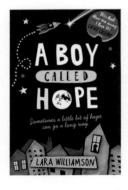

A BOY CALLED HOPE
Lara Williamson
(Usborne)

Dan Hope has a list of things he wants to come true. He wants his sister, Ninja Grace, to go to university at the North Pole and only come back once a year. He wants to help Sherlock Holmes solve a daring mystery, preferably a zombie one. He wants to be the first 11-year-old to land on the moon, and he wants his Dad to love him. When Dan's dad, who moved out when Dan was seven, appears on TV as a presenter, Dan decides to track him down. Things do not go smoothly.

With fights at school, boyfriend trouble for his sister and his mum and a pet dog who is constantly sick on the carpet, Dan has his hands full. Luckily, he has plenty of genius ideas and never gives up.

In this bittersweet, laugh-out-loud story, a little bit of hope goes a long way.
■ *Lindsay McKrell, Writer & Children's Librarian*

IF YOU LIKE THIS, WHY NOT TRY . . .	
	THE ADVENTURES OF ALFIE ONION Vivian French & Marta Kissi
	BEAKY MALONE: WORLD'S GREATEST LIAR Barry Hutchison

KATIE MORAG AND THE TWO GRANDMOTHERS
Mairi Hedderwick
(Random House)

Grannie Island is unimpressed with Granma Mainland's swanky city ways until Katie Morag hatches an ingenious plan that may defuse the tension between the family matriarchs.

A prize sheep, a muddy loch and the secret to Granma Mainland's silvery white hairdo all play key roles in this wryly funny tale of a family culture clash. The two grannies are chalk and cheese: Granma Mainland is all fancy clothes and expensive perfumes while Grannie Island trundles around on her tractor in dungarees and wellies.

For my money, the second Katie Morag book is the best. In a deceptively simple story infused with witty observations, Mairi Hedderwick brilliantly captures the ebb and flow of island life. Gorgeous double-page illustrations reveal new details on every viewing. And keep your eye on old Neilly-Beag, his flirtations with Grannie Mainland might just pay off one of these days.
■ *Neil Hepburn, Filmmaker & Marketing Manager at Cameo Cinema*

IF YOU LIKE THIS, WHY NOT TRY . . .

 A YEAR IN OUR NEW GARDEN
Gerda Muller

 ROSIE REVERE, ENGINEER
Andrea Beaty & David Roberts

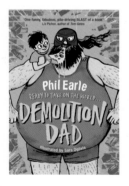

DEMOLITION DAD
Phil Earle & Sara Ogilvie
(Orion)

Jake Biggs loves two things more than anything else: his demolition-man dad, and wrestling. Watching his dad wrestling is best of all. The trouble is, Dad wants to keep the wrestling a secret but Jake is bursting with pride and wants the world to know.

When Jake hears that Grapplemania are looking for a new star he can't resist. He's going to get Dad to join the competition . . . even if it means entering him in secret. What could possibly go wrong?

Do you like the idea of reading about a man-mountain of a dad? Who usually spends his days smashing down buildings? And then tries his luck in the world of Spandex costumes, body slams and blood-curdling battle cries? Then look no further. When you're in the mood for laugh-out-loud fun, with dollops of danger, then *Demolition Dad* is just the book you're looking for.
■ *Louise Kelly, Writer & Portobello Book Festival Organiser*

IF YOU LIKE THIS, WHY NOT TRY . . .

 GRANNY NOTHING
Cathy MacPhail

 HONEY AND ME
Karen McCombie

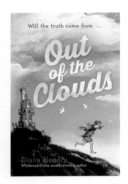

Will the truth come from ...

OUT OF THE CLOUDS
Diana Hendry
(Hachette)

Oliver Coggin lives a lonely life in a house perched right on top of a mountain in Scotland as he waits for his pa to come home. The rest of Oliver's family don't seem too worried, knowing their pa is doing some kind of 'secret scientific research', but he was meant to be home months ago, and Oliver's tired of being the responsible one.

From this point on, the story becomes a real adventure as Oliver tries to find out why his pa went away in the first place and goes on a quest to bring him back, making exciting discoveries and new friends along the way.

Out of the Clouds is a heart-warming family story with a mystery that will keep you reading until the very end. You can't help but be charmed by the eccentric Coggin family and you'll be rooting for Oliver to bring his pa back home.
■ *Sarah Mallon, Scottish Book Trust*

IF YOU LIKE THIS, WHY NOT TRY . . .

FIACLAN GRANAIDH
Brianòg Brady Dawson

THE 10PM QUESTION
Kate Di Goldi

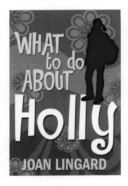

WHAT TO DO ABOUT HOLLY
Joan Lingard
(Catnip)

Holly is a quiet girl who is used to looking after herself and spends a lot of time on her own with her books and her imagination. But even the biggest bookworms can do with a few close friends.

Holly's mum works nights and spends a lot of time with her boyfriend, who Holly doesn't like. When Holly's packed off on the train to her dad's house and her mum asks a stranger to look after her, she is lucky that the stranger is Nina Nightingale – who happens to be the author of some of her favourite books!

When the pair discover that Holly's dad is working abroad, leaving Holly stranded over the holidays, Nina invites her to join their family on their (rather dramatic) trip.

This book is about relationships and friendships and how they can grow out of the most difficult – and unusual – situations.
■ *Paul Hudson, Librarian*

IF YOU LIKE THIS, WHY NOT TRY . . .

LILY ALONE
Jacqueline Wilson

RUBY HOLLER
Sharon Creech

Heroes vs Villains

EVIL EMPEROR PENGUIN

Laura Ellen Anderson
(David Fickling Books)

There are few things cuter than penguins, but few beings more evil than the Evil Emperor Penguin (EEP). From his Evil Underground Headquarters, he hatches all kinds of diabolical schemes to take over the world.

Writer and artist Laura Ellen Anderson has created a bright and action-packed world with a brilliant cast of supporting characters. EEP's assistants are Number 8, the brainy, suit-wearing octopus sidekick, and Eugene, a minion cloned from the abominable snowman who's so cute all he can think of are hugs and unicorns.

Across 16 four-page chapters told in graphic novel form, we're introduced to EEP, his friends and his dastardly plans, and we see how his competition with Evil Cat to be the most evil being in the world starts. It's silly and plenty of fun, with hints of *Despicable Me* and *Danger Mouse*, and the humour is so well done that you might want to recommend it to an adult when you're finished.
■ *David Pollock, Arts Journalist*

IF YOU LIKE THIS, WHY NOT TRY . . .

 THE DEMON HEADMASTER
Gillian Cross

 ARTEMIS FOWL
Eoin Colfer

LONG GONE DON

Etherington Brothers
(David Fickling Books)

Ten-year-old Don Skelton never imagined a school day could get worse than drowning face down in a bowl of oxtail soup but, unfortunately, he was wrong. Transported to the spooky underworld of Broilerdoom, Don is soon forced to fight off a host of baddies. Welcome to *Long Gone Don*, a comic book unlike any other.

Fans of the Phoenix Comic will already be familiar with Don and his afterlife escapades, and this book brings his adventures together in his first collected volume. Most authors and illustrators could not get away with killing off their main character on the first page of their novel, but the Etherington Brothers are not most authors and illustrators. Between Robin's wacky, fast-paced, hilarious storytelling and Lorenzo's complex, high impact artwork, this darkly funny story crackles and fizzes off the page. Perfect for fans of comics and anyone who feels unmotivated by more 'traditional' books.
■ *Helen Croney, Scottish Book Trust*

IF YOU LIKE THIS, WHY NOT TRY . . .

 KNIGHTLEY AND SON
Rohan Gavin

 RAPUNZEL'S REVENGE
Shannon Hale, Dean Hale & Nathan Hale

THE SUPERPOWER PROJECT
Paul Bristow
(Floris Books)

Megan's beloved Gran has just exploded while water-skiing, and the weirdness is far from over. Following clues from a treasure hunt through Greenock, Megan and her best friend Cameron discover that they've inherited a legacy as old as their community and a dangerous task that will require them to become real heroes. Can they master their new superpowers, outwit a megalomaniacal foe, and assemble the weirdest world-saving team in West Scotland?

This book is one wild ride full of imagination, packed with characters so cleverly brought to life that I could imagine them sitting next to me on the bus. Megan is a brilliant hero, with just enough self-awareness to know her flaws and more than enough courage to believe in her and her friends' potential to save the day. A particular delight is her partnership with Cameron – a charming and hilariously authentic friendship that grounds this adventure squarely in modern Scotland.
■ *Nicole Brandon, Scottish Book Trust*

IF YOU LIKE THIS, WHY NOT TRY . . .	
	THE BAD GUYS: EPISODE 1 Aaron Blabey
	ELECTRIGIRL Jo Cotteril & Cathy Brett

THE DAY THE WORLD WENT LOKI
Robert J Harris
(Floris Books)

The McBride brothers are about to unleash all manner of chaos on their unsuspecting home town. Greg's endless quest to avoid studying for a looming maths test and his younger sibling Lewis's need to submit a school project on time cause the pair to release magic into the world that may ensure no one ever has to sit another exam again. In fact, it might just put off tomorrow forever.

Set in St Andrews, the use of actual street names and landmarks (recognisable beneath a little magic) make you feel that perhaps an innocent looking spell really could wreak havoc if carelessly used. In order to fix their mistake, Greg and Lewis must negotiate a little Norse mythology and a lot of mayhem, all with the help and hindrance of some weirdly familiar friends and foes. The book also manages to ask the important questions, like if your mother was an ogre, would breakfast be worse than Aunt Vivian's cooking?
■ *Candice Purwin, Illustrator & Comic Writer*

IF YOU LIKE THIS, WHY NOT TRY . . .	
	BEASTS OF OLYMPUS: CENTAUR SCHOOL Lucy Coats & David Roberts
	PERCY JACKSON AND THE LIGHTNING THIEF Rick Riordan

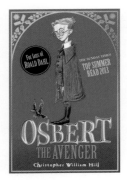

OSBERT THE AVENGER
Christopher William Hill
(Orchard)

Osbert Brinkoff is an exceptionally talented young boy who attends a school that only admits the cleverest children from his home town of Schwartzgarten.

However, Osbert soon realises that the school and all of the teachers who work there are cruel and malicious. When Osbert is told to leave by his tyrannical headmaster, he decides not to give up without a fight and so he begins to use his genius in order to create imaginative, ghastly and gory plans to hurt all of the wicked teachers who treated him badly.

Christopher William Hill's style is similar to Roald Dahl, as he manages to create a story that is just as gruesome as it is hilarious. Osbert is such a charming and amusing character that it is very easy to forgive his outrageous antics and, instead, to hope that he succeeds in his cunning vengeance!
■ *Madeleine Knowles, Bookseller at Topping & Co*

IF YOU LIKE THIS, WHY NOT TRY . . .

 A SERIES OF UNFORTUNATE EVENTS: THE BAD BEGINNING
Lemony Snicket

 UNCLE MONTAGUE'S TALES OF TERROR
Chris Priestley

BEETLE BOY
MG Leonard
(Chicken House)

Darkus finds his life turned upside down when his scientist father mysteriously disappears from a sealed vault at work. His dad's not the sort who would abandon his son but nobody can work out where he's gone or why. It's up to Uncle Maximillian, a famous archaeologist, to give Darkus a home among the unusual objects he's collected on his travels.

Darkus finds an unlikely friend in a magnificent rhinoceros beetle called Baxter and their friendship leads him to a stunning discovery. The real questions are, where did Baxter really come from and can he help Darkus find his father?

This is a fast-moving adventure full of memorable characters, from the hilarious bumbling fools who live next door, to the resourceful kids who refuse to be beaten. You'll find out more than you ever thought possible about beetles and discover a truly scary villain in Lucretia Cutter, a cruel woman with an astonishing secret.
■ *Karen Thirkell, Writer*

IF YOU LIKE THIS, WHY NOT TRY . . .

 THE MYSTERIOUS BENEDICT SOCIETY
Trenton Lee Stewart

 SQUIRREL BOY VS THE BOGEYMAN
Dave Lowe

THORFINN THE NICEST VIKING AND THE AWFUL INVASION
David MacPhail & Richard Morgan
(Floris Books)

Thorfinn, only son of the village chief, is not your usual Viking. He likes a nice cup of tea, preferably with a scone, is always polite and enjoys making jam much, much more than fighting.

Thorfinn is approaching the age when he earns his Viking name. His father, Harald the Skull-Splitter, wants him to be something respectable, like 'sword-slasher' or 'ear-masher', and put an end to this nonsense about baking and learning to read. There's only one thing for it: Harald will take Thorfinn on a voyage of destruction to put him to the test!

But between invading Scotland and meeting the fearsome Ragnar the Granny-Wrestler, Thorfinn will need all his wits to earn himself a name . . . and avoid getting thrown overboard.

A hugely fun, laugh-out-loud adventure about using your brains and being yourself, this is the first in a series of Thorfinn books.
■ *Emma Beeby, Comic Book Writer*

IF YOU LIKE THIS, WHY NOT TRY . . .

	THE LITTLEST VIKING Sandi Toksvig
	THERE'S A VIKING IN MY BED AND OTHER STORIES Jeremy Strong & John Levers

THE PRINCESS IN BLACK
Shannon Hale, Dean Hale & LeUyen Pham
(Walker Books)

The very pretty Princess Magnolia is having hot chocolate in her castle with the very nosy Duchess Wigtower. 'You are too prim and perfect,' says the Duchess. The perfect Princess smiles. Unknown to the nosy Duchess, Princess Magnolia has a secret cupboard where she stashes her outfit in black. When her ring rings, it's time to change into the bold, monster-fighting Princess in Black.

There are monsters to fight and goats to save. Even the princess's friend Duff is more than a simple goat-herd. He's a 'goat-avenger' in disguise – or wants to be.

This funny Superman-themed book, with beautiful illustrations by LeUyen Pham, has innocent-looking characters change into heroes. The Princess in Black herself has a black cape, a mask and can fly through the air. She can control monsters and even manages to outwit the nosy Duchess, too.
■ *Janis Mackay, Writer*

IF YOU LIKE THIS, WHY NOT TRY . . .

	AMAZING GRACE Mary Hoffman & Caroline Binch
	PIPPI LONGSTOCKING Astrid Lindgren & Lauren Child

MY BROTHER IS A SUPERHERO
David Solomons, Laura Ellen Anderson & Rob Biddulph
(Nosy Crow)

Eleven-year-old Luke Parker knows everything there is to know about superheroes, but when his too-cool-for-school older brother Zack is given superpowers instead, Luke is mightily miffed.

With the plight of two universes at stake, Luke must persuade Zack to embrace his new role – even if he won't wear a cape. With Luke's help, Zack (who wouldn't know his X-Men from his X-Box), is transformed into Star Lad and sets about discovering his superpowers. Faster than the Flash, supervillain Nemesis kidnaps Star Lad, putting the whole planet in danger. Luke and friends Serge and Lara must rescue Star Lad and save the universe, armed only with courage and a My Little Pony camera.

This is a gloriously funny story packed full of witty observations and comic book bad guys. For fans of Frank Cottrell Boyce and David Walliams, and anyone who has ever imagined what their own superpower would be.
■ *Morag Smart, Bookseller at Waterstones*

IF YOU LIKE THIS, WHY NOT TRY . . .

OLIVER FIBBS: THE ATTACK OF THE ALIEN BRAIN
Steve Hartley

HAMISH AND THE WORLDSTOPPERS
Danny Wallace

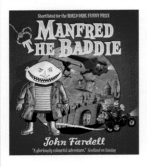

MANFRED THE BADDIE
John Fardell
(Quercus)

No doubt about it, Manfred the Baddie is the baddest baddie in the whole world. Ever! Just look at him with his brawny henchmen, diabolical contraptions and shark-faced grin. He's a thief, a pirate, a kidnapper, a bully. No wonder nobody likes him.

But that's the big problem for Manfred. Despite the heaps of priceless jewels and his wonderful art collection, he doesn't have anyone to comfort him when he falls ill. Maybe he should become Manfred the Goodie?

John Fardell's glorious fantasy is a mix of traditional picture book spreads and comic book styling, using frames and speech bubbles. It makes the story fun and accessible whether reading aloud or alone. His illustrations are wildly detailed, brimming with imagination, demanding many re-readings.

It's witty, warm-hearted and feelgood through and through. A true gem from one of Scotland's most uniquely talented illustrators.
■ *Keith Gray, Writer*

IF YOU LIKE THIS, WHY NOT TRY . . .

WILF THE MIGHTY WORRIER: SAVES THE WORLD
Georgia Pritchett & Jamie Littler

NICHOLAS AND THE WILD ONES
Niki Daly

Adventure

SHACKLETON'S JOURNEY
William Grill
(Flying Eye)

Just over a hundred years ago, explorer Ernest Shackleton set out to try to cross Antarctica from one side to the other by travelling directly through the South Pole. However, the ill-fated expedition soon went wrong – his ship, *Endurance*, was trapped in the pack ice before they even reached the Antarctic continent.

After spending many months drifting with the ice, the ship was eventually crushed and Shackleton and his men were faced with a tough 500-mile journey back to the nearest civilisation.

This book tells the gripping story of how the men travelled on the ice, and in open boats across the stormy seas, to reach Elephant Island, followed by Shackleton's own trek to South Georgia and eventual rescue. The delightful drawings that illustrate his story perfectly capture the atmosphere of this famous tale of adventure.
■ *Brian Kelly, Education Officer at Dundee Heritage Trust and RRS Discovery*

IF YOU LIKE THIS, WHY NOT TRY . . .	
	PIRATE GIRL Kerstin Meyer, Chantal Wright & Cornelia Funke
	THE PROMISE Nicola Davies, Laura Carlin

HOW TO TRAIN YOUR DRAGON
Cressida Cowell
(Hodder)

Suffering scallops, it's not easy training to be a Viking! Young Hiccup Horrendous Haddock III has everything to prove and everything to lose as he attempts to claim his place as future Chieftain of Berk – starting with training his very own dragon. Hiccup might be smarter than his age-mates but he's also smaller, weaker and much more afraid; can he overcome his fears to become a Viking hero? Or is he going to wind up in a dragon's guts?

Full of bright wit and brutal honesty, this is a brilliant book that launched a huge series. Each page is scrawled over with unruly illustrations, studded with scraps of dragon lore, and punctuated with hilarious commentary from Hiccup and his companions. This is a fantastic adventure that explores failure as much as success, and weighs the cost of being different against the price of fitting in with sneaky maturity and shining humour.
■ *Nicole Brandon, Scottish Book Trust*

IF YOU LIKE THIS, WHY NOT TRY . . .	
	DRAGON RIDER Cornelia Funke
	TELL ME A DRAGON Jackie Morris

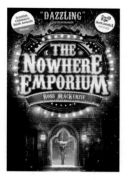

THE NOWHERE EMPORIUM
Ross MacKenzie
(Floris Books)

When Daniel hides in a dusty old shop to get away from school bullies he finds himself apprenticed to Mr Silver, and the Nowhere Emporium. Within its labyrinth of rooms, which appear never-ending and hold wonders beyond imagination, Daniel begins to learn how to create his own magical rooms while making friends with Mr Silver's daughter Ellie. But then Mr Silver disappears, and the Nowhere Emporium starts to crumble. Can Daniel and Ellie save it and find Mr Silver?

Magical ideas and spell-binding descriptions make this story a world you really wish you could be part of. I love the idea of being able to write your imagined ideas down in an enchanted book and have them become reality in a room you could visit. There's edge-of-your-seat adventures, great friendships and an evil villain! What more could you want from a story that's as much fun for adventure seekers as it is for book-lovers?
■ *Cat Anderson, Bookseller at The Edinburgh Book Shop*

IF YOU LIKE THIS, WHY NOT TRY . . .	
	THE INVENTION OF HUGO CABRET Brian Selznick
	HOWL'S MOVING CASTLE Diana Wynne Jones

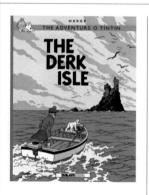

THE ADVENTURS OF TINTIN: THE DERK ISLE
Hergé (Translated by Susan Rennie)
(Egmont)

Jings! Embroiled in a mystery and accused of a crime he didn't commit, Tintin is on the case. This graphic novel adventure sees the young reporter travel the length of the UK on the hunt for clues about the strange events surrounding the Derk Isle.

Wi' his faithful dug Tarrie, pursued by polismen Nisbet and Nesbit, this is a gleeful Scots translation of Hergé's original *L'île Noire* and a real treat to read.

In print for over 85 years, I reckon Hergé's Tintin is up there with the most famous of adventurers, like Indiana Jones or James Bond. The stories are as joyful and exciting as they've ever been and the artwork is absolutely peerless. A fantastic introduction to the series, or a fresh joy for lifelong fans, *The Derk Isle* is a great read for comic and graphic novel fans of any age – or anyone who likes a good mystery thriller!
■ *Fin Cramb, Comic Writer & Artist*

IF YOU LIKE THIS, WHY NOT TRY . . .	
	MORTAL ENGINES Philip Reeve
	THE RAINBOW ORCHID: VOLUME 1 Garen Ewing

ONE BOY AND HIS DOG
Eva Ibbotson
(Marion Lloyd Books)

Hal lives in a big house with wealthy parents. He has everything except the thing he wants most – a dog. His mum will not allow a smelly, hairy creature in her perfect home. Kelsey lives in a cramped flat with very little money but she has her dream job of working in the Easy Pets Dog Agency where dogs are rented out to the rich.

For his birthday, Hal gets a weekend with a dog and Kelsey introduces him to Fleck. Perfect, except Hal thinks he is getting a dog for life and Fleck thinks he's getting a boy for life!

What follows is a fast-paced, funny and moving adventure involving canines and kids outwitting greedy grown-ups. Each dog character is perfectly described, from calm, clever Otto the St Bernard to a bad-tempered, Mexican hairless called Queen Tilly, and all play a role to keep Hal and Fleck together.

■ *Janet Smyth, Children & Education Programme Director at Edinburgh International Book Festival*

IF YOU LIKE THIS, WHY NOT TRY . . .

HOW TO LOOK FOR A LOST DOG
Ann M Martin

BECAUSE OF WINN-DIXIE
Kate DiCamillo

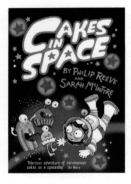

CAKES IN SPACE
Philip Reeve & Sarah McIntyre
(OUP)

Astra is wide awake on a spaceship taking her to her new life on the planet Nova Mundi. But Astra shouldn't be awake right now, because it takes 199 years to reach this new world from Earth.

While her family are all snoring in their sleeping pods, Astra, along with her new friend Philbeam, go off exploring. They soon find out the ship is in deep trouble. Not only has the ship been knocked off course, it's also been invaded by a gang of Poglites, an alien salvage crew. However, they are the least of her worries; something far more sinister is lurking in the canteen . . . CAKES, like you've never seen before, with wide mouths and lots of shiny, little teeth!

This action-packed, funny tale will leave your taste buds tingling for more. Be prepared to never look at a fairy cake in the same way again.

■ *Elaine Hallyburton, Librarian*

IF YOU LIKE THIS, WHY NOT TRY . . .

HORRIBLE SCIENCE: SPACE, STARS AND SLIMY ALIENS
Nick Arnold & Tony De Saulles

SPACE DUMPLINS
Craig Thompson

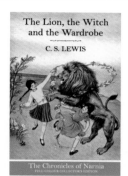

THE CHRONICLES OF NARNIA: THE LION, THE WITCH AND THE WARDROBE
CS Lewis
(HarperCollins)

Four children evacuated from London during World War II find the mother of all distractions in the rambling country house of the professor who's taken them in. Lucy, the youngest, discovers that a wardrobe leads into Narnia, a land populated by magical creatures but gripped by the spell of an eternal winter.

First published in 1950, the story of Lucy, her brother Edmund who falls into league with the cold-hearted White Witch, and their older brother and sister, is a fast-moving tale dominated by the majestic lion whose arrival breaks the witch's spell.

Edmund's treachery, and the battle he triggers between good and evil, are vividly written, and with a narrator who directly addresses the reader, the story feels surprisingly fresh to anyone who's enjoyed a similar style from authors like Lemony Snicket. An absolute treasure of a story.
■ *Sheila M Averbuch, Writer & Copywriter*

IF YOU LIKE THIS, WHY NOT TRY . . .

 NORTHERN LIGHTS
Philip Pulman

 LAURA MARLIN MYSTERIES: DEAD MAN'S COVE
Lauren St John

GEORGE'S SECRET KEY TO THE UNIVERSE
Lucy and Stephen Hawking
(Corgi)

George doesn't have a computer and wants one. He's also lonely and wishes his life was exciting. When his pet pig leads him into out-of-bounds NEXT DOOR, the extra-terrestrial excitement begins. NEXT DOOR is where genius scientist Eric and his daughter Annie live, plus Cosmos, the world's most advanced, top-secret computer. They are exploring the universe. George joins them. So does Eric's arch-enemy!

This is a good versus evil story with a difference. It's gripping. It's funny. There's an evil scientist to outwit, black holes to get out of and the universe to travel through. Learn about planets, asteroids, comets, the Milky Way, black holes and more, with awe-inspiring photographs and mind-expanding facts.

This book is by Lucy Hawking and her dad, Stephen Hawking – the most brilliant scientist since Einstein. For anyone keen on unlocking the secrets of the universe, this book is a must.
■ *Janis Mackay, Writer*

IF YOU LIKE THIS, WHY NOT TRY . . .

 THE MANY WORLDS OF ALBIE BRIGHT
Christopher Edge

 TIME TRAVELLING WITH A HAMSTER
Ross Welford

THE SHAPESHIFTER: FEATHER AND FANG
Ali Sparkes
(OUP)

Fans of X-Men and the Marvel universe won't be able to resist this fast-paced, superhero-charged adventure that follows the exploits of Dax Jones and his gifted friends. If this is the first you've read in the Shapeshifter series, don't worry; it's easy to pick up without knowledge of previous adventures.

In *Feather and Fang*, Dax needs to lead a rescue of his friends after the government-sponsored school that houses and protects Children Of Limitless Ability (COLAs) cracks down on student freedoms and becomes more prison than school.

The only trouble is, Dax must team up with rogue ex-students who've flown the nest long ago and whose methods and motivations are questionable. When your abilities are limitless, your ruthlessness can be, too.

Wonderfully drawn characters – as well as Dax's ability to transform at will to fox, otter, falcon or human – make this a pure delight.
■ *Sheila M Averbuch, Writer & Copywriter*

IF YOU LIKE THIS, WHY NOT TRY . . .

KNITBONE PEPPER – GHOST DOG
Claire Baker & Ross Collins

MAGNUS FIN AND THE OCEAN QUEST
Janis Mackay

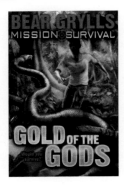

MISSION SURVIVAL: GOLD OF THE GODS
Bear Grylls
(Random House)

This is the first in a series of seven adventure stories about Beck Granger, a 13-year-old boy with survival skills to rival the book's famous author, Bear Grylls.

The action takes place in Colombia and begins with a carnival and a kidnapping that sets Beck and two feisty companions off on a rescue mission through the rainforest. They require all of Beck's knowledge to stave off starvation, snakes and howler monkeys in a fast-paced story complete with a pet parakeet and a legendary City of Gold.

Whatever you think of the Bear Grylls brand, it lends wonderful credibility to the many real survival tips woven into the story that I think young readers will love. The ending is a bit abrupt but a final information section on knots and a taster of the first three chapters of the next book in the series are a nice touch.
■ *Dr Hermione Cockburn, Scientific Director at Dynamic Earth, Edinburgh*

IF YOU LIKE THIS, WHY NOT TRY . . .

UPSIDE DOWN IN THE JUNGLE
Helen Phillips

JOURNEY TO THE RIVER SEA
Eva Ibbotson

Animals

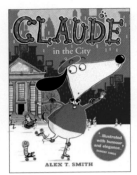

CLAUDE IN THE CITY
Alex T Smith
(Hodder)

Meet Claude. He's a dog with a secret life. As soon as his owners leave the house, Claude opens his eyes, springs out of bed and goes on an adventure. Claude's best friend, Sir Bobblysock (yes, he is a bobbly sock), is always right by his side. *Claude in the City* follows their adventures as they shop, visit an art gallery and go to the hospital. But unexpected things happen when Claude is around. Will you spot the art thief before Claude does? What is the mystery illness in the hospital waiting room? And does Claude know how funny Dr Ivan Achinbum's name is?

This friendly dog loves berets, bones and a nice cup of tea. The book is jam-packed with red and black illustrations that bring Claude's world to life. And once you've peeked into Claude's world, you'll definitely want to read more books in the series.
■ *Emma Andrew, Teacher*

IF YOU LIKE THIS, WHY NOT TRY . . .

THE LONELY BEAST
Chris Judge

POLLY AND THE PUFFIN
Jenny Colgan & Thomas Docherty

LOVE THAT DOG
sharon creech

LOVE THAT DOG
Sharon Creech
(Bloomsbury)

What is a poem? What do poems mean, and do we try to deconstruct them too much? These are just some of the questions you'll be asking yourself after reading *Love That Dog*.

In the book, which is written entirely as a narrative poem, a young boy is asked by his teacher to write some verse, and is hesitant, getting himself caught up in definitions of what a 'proper' poem is. When his teacher shows him a host of different poems, he realises that poetry can be anything to anyone. By the time his poem about a beloved pet inspires his fellow classmates, he's well and truly hooked on composition.

No matter what age you are, you'll find it difficult to resist *Love That Dog*. It's charming and moving, a real testament to the power poetry can have when it comes unfiltered from the heart. It's clever without being pompous, and a potentially liberating text for anyone who thinks that poetry is somehow not for them.
■ *Chris Leslie, Scottish Book Trust*

IF YOU LIKE THIS, WHY NOT TRY . . .

I AM A POETATO
John Hegley

OLD POSSUM'S BOOK OF PRACTICAL CATS
TS Eliot & Axel Scheffler

THE UNBELIEVABLE TOP SECRET DIARY OF PIG
Emer Stamp
(Scholastic)

Pig feels very lucky. Farmer gives him lots of yummy slops and lots of special back scratches. He has a best friend, Duck, but he does not like the Evil Chickens who steal his food. The chickens are building a space tractor-rocket. Pig writes: 'Hello. You will not believe what has happened today. I don't believe what happened today and it happened to me.'

The chickens want to send Pig to Pluto where there wouldn't be any food at all – no way is he going!

Duck tells Pig why Farmer gives him so much food and calls him Roast Pig. Pig is very sad. When he hears Farmer say he is 'nearly ready', the Evil Chickens' space mission is the only option. Read Pig's amazing Diary to see what happens next!

'Today was quite a bonkers day. I has so much to tell you so here goes . . .'

■ *Lindsay McKrell, Writer & Children's Librarian*

IF YOU LIKE THIS, WHY NOT TRY . . .

	LOVE FROM LOUISA Simon Puttock & Jo Kiddie
	THE TALES OF OLGA DA POLGA Michael Bond & Catherine Raynor

THE GRUFFALO IN SCOTS
Julia Donaldson & Axel Scheffler (translated by James Robertson)
(Itchy Coo)

One of the many joys of Julia Donaldson's books is that they are just so easy and such fun to read out loud! This is the engaging tale of a resourceful wee moose who dreams up a Gruffalo to keep him safe from other creatures in the wild and has to use all his wit to save himself from that very fearsome creature at the end.

The wonderful bouncy prose is taken to another level with this translation into Scots and is completely genius. Find out the Scots words for all the different animals that the wee moose meets and laugh together at how funny the words sound.

The translation rhymes beautifully with just the right amount of repetition. With wonderfully expressive illustrations by Axel Scheffler, *The Gruffalo in Scots* is a truly glorious introduction to Scots for young readers and a classic in its own right.

■ *Angie Crawford, Bookseller at Waterstones*

IF YOU LIKE THIS, WHY NOT TRY . . .

	WHAT PET SHOULD I GET? Dr Seuss
	THE LANGUAGE OF CAT Rachel Rooney

SKY HAWK
Gill Lewis
(OUP)

A beautiful bird of prey, an international voyage and the power of friendship: *Sky Hawk* is an unforgettable emotional rollercoaster set against the backdrop of the Scottish Highlands.

The son of a farmer, Callum is an ordinary Scottish country kid, but his life is changed forever when he strikes up a friendship with Iona, an out-of-the-ordinary girl from his village. The pair discover a rare osprey nesting on Callum's farm and vow to keep their discovery a closely guarded secret. But this is just the beginning of a story that turns into a heart-wrenching, intense and emotional journey that gripped me right until the very last page.

This gorgeously optimistic story is the first of a series of novels that have turned Gill Lewis into a superstar among children's writers.

I first read *Sky Hawk* to my daughter when she was 8, and since then she's read it again several times. Four years on, it's still one of her all-time favourites.
■ *Nick Barley, Director at Edinburgh International Book Festival*

IF YOU LIKE THIS, WHY NOT TRY . . .

 CHARLOTTE'S WEB EB White

 THE WHITE GIRAFFE Lauren St John

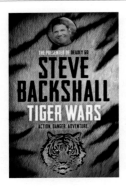

TIGER WARS
Steve Backshall
(Orion)

Set in the majestic lands of India and China, this action-packed, eco adventure by wildlife specialist Steve Backshall contains an important message about the survival of tigers.

The Clan, a secret group of children, tattooed with their own animal identity, are trying to poach tigers. Two teenagers from very differing backgrounds, Saker and Sinter, make the brave decision to escape from the Clan and try to save the tigers from exploitation. They need to trust each other, work together and keep their wits about them, as they become the hunted.

Once I started this book, I couldn't put it down and my heart was thumping as the drama unfolded before me. It heightened my awareness of the dangers faced by many species who are fighting for survival, but this book is so much more than that. I'm looking forward to reading the rest of the series.
■ *Elaine Clarke, Teacher*

IF YOU LIKE THIS, WHY NOT TRY . . .

 AMY WILD: AMAZON SUMMER Helen Skelton

 THE LAST WILD Piers Torday

FREDDIE MOLE: LION TAMER
Alexander McCall Smith & Kate Hindley
(Bloomsbury)

Freddie Mole lives with his dad, who repairs washing machines, and his twin brother and sister. His mum works on cruise ships, cleaning cabins and so isn't at home a huge amount. They don't have very much money and so when the circus rolls into town and Freddie has the chance to spend his summer working there, he jumps at it.

Now, Freddie is a boy who is very kind, pleasant and hardworking and that can take you far in life. He starts out as the circus cleaner and then moves to be part of the trapeze act (which is quite scary) but then is asked to help the lion tamer with four fierce wild cats. Eek, he's terrified. It takes all Freddie's courage, but he discovers being a lion tamer is not at all what he anticipated.

This is a funny tale of courage, kindness and bravery.

■ *Janet Smyth, Children & Education Programme Director at Edinburgh International Book Festival*

IF YOU LIKE THIS, WHY NOT TRY . . .

A BOY AND A BEAR IN A BOAT
Dave Shelton

THE SHEEP-PIG
Dick King-Smith

BLAMEHOUNDS
Ross Collins
(Barrington Stoke)

Blamehounds follows enterprising pooch Norman and his friend, Ringo, who are used as easy scapegoats by their humans for accidents and embarrassing situations.

Fed up of taking the blame for things that are not their fault, they decide to start making money out of people's need to shirk responsibility. The project quickly becomes successful, leading Norman and Ringo to expand the business. Soon dogs worldwide are taking the blame for everything, from nasty smells and messes to starting a war.

This is a very funny read, cleverly written with witty illustrations that bring the story to life.

One of my favourites is of Norman and Ringo, lounging in chewed armchairs while their team operates a busy global call centre from disused public toilets in the park. I shared this book with my sons (P4 and P7) who giggled throughout, from mention of the first fart to the final sentence.

■ *Moira Findlay, Scottish Book Trust*

IF YOU LIKE THIS, WHY NOT TRY . . .

PUGS OF THE FROZEN NORTH
Philip Reeve & Sarah McIntyre

MUDPUDDLE FARM
Michael Morpurgo & Shoo Rayner

DEADLY!: THE TRUTH ABOUT THE MOST DANGEROUS CREATURES ON EARTH (ANIMAL SCIENCE)
Nicola Davies
(Walker)

Are you intrigued by why cats' tongues are so rough, why sharks have triangular teeth or ever found yourself wondering how to survive in bear country? If so, this is definitely the book for you.

Packed full of fascinating facts about some of the world's deadliest creatures, it explores how different animals have evolved to use a variety of weapons to catch a tasty meal. If this all sounds a bit scary then don't worry as you will pick up some handy survival tips should you come face to face with any of these ferocious beasties. Finally you will discover how, despite being a little fearsome, they also have an important role to play within our natural world.

As an animal enthusiast myself, I really enjoyed reading this book and learnt lots along the way. I especially liked the amusing pictures that bring the words to life.
■ *Anna Danby, Senior Education Officer at Dynamic Earth, Edinburgh*

IF YOU LIKE THIS, WHY NOT TRY . . .

ANIMALIUM
Jenny Broom
& Katie Scott

HOW MUCH POO DOES AN ELEPHANT DO? ... AND FURTHER FASCINATING FACTS!
Mitchell Symons

THE BOLDS
Julian Clary & David Roberts
(Andersen Press)

Mr and Mrs Bold have a secret – they are actually a pair of laughing hyenas who assumed the identity of a couple of unfortunate tourists who had ended up on the wrong side of a crocodile during their African honeymoon.

Using the passports of the unfortunately expired tourists, the Bolds travel to the UK and set up home in England, start a family and do a very good job of hiding the fact that they are not actually human at all. What a laugh!

When they get a little homesick, they decide to visit a local safari park where they meet a group of hyenas with a sad tale to tell. A daring rescue is planned but will the Bolds pull it off?

And under the suspicious eye of their grumpy next door neighbour, are they going to be able to keep their real identities undercover?
■ *Jenni Hamilton, Librarian*

IF YOU LIKE THIS, WHY NOT TRY . . .

VOICES IN THE PARK
Anthony Browne

THE BEAR AND THE PIANO
David Litchfield

Spooky

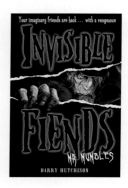

INVISIBLE FIENDS: MR MUMBLES
Barry Hutchison
(HarperCollins)

Like a scary story? Like to feel the hairs on the back of your neck rise as you turn each page? Well, this is the book for you!

As a young boy, Kyle invented his imaginary friend Mr Mumbles, but as he grew older, Mr Mumbles was laid to rest in the furthest corners of Kyle's imagination. Now Mr Mumbles has come back and he doesn't like to be ignored. He's looking for revenge – in a big way.

Kyle is fighting for his life . . . or is he? Is Mr Mumbles real? He seems frighteningly real to Kyle. And who is the strange girl who has come to help him? So many questions to be answered. Can Kyle find the reason for the return of Mr Mumbles or has he already run out of time? Find out in this creepy and enchanting story about invisible friends – and enemies.

■ *Jennifer Broadley, Teacher*

IF YOU LIKE THIS, WHY NOT TRY . . .

STITCH HEAD
Guy Bass &
Pete Williamson

THE DARK
Lemony Snicket
& Jon Klassen

GOTH GIRL AND THE GHOST OF A MOUSE
Chris Riddell
(Macmillan)

Ada Goth, the daughter of reclusive and quietly elegant Lord Goth, lives a lonely life at Ghastly-Gorm Hall. Once she meets Ishmael, the ghost of a mouse, and visitors William and Emily Cabbage, she finally has the friends she needs to unravel the many mysteries taking place in her spooky home.

But will they be able to figure out what the suspicious indoor gamekeeper, Maltravers, is up to in time for the Annual Metaphorical Bicycle Race and Indoor Hunt?

Beautifully illustrated by Chris Riddell, this book is fun for both parents and children, with many knowing winks to other beloved children's books, as well as classics from gothic literature. The book is the first of three (so far) and sets you up perfectly to carry on discovering the grounds of Ghastly-Gorm with Ada and her friends in the Attic Club.

■ *Sasha de Buyl, Scottish Book Trust*

IF YOU LIKE THIS, WHY NOT TRY . . .

DUST 'N' BONES
Chris Mould

CONSTABLE AND TOOP
Gareth P Jones

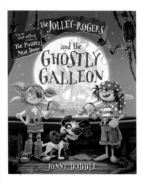

THE JOLLEY-ROGERS AND THE GHOSTLY GALLEON
Jonny Duddle
(Templar)

From the creator of *The Pirates Next Door* comes another illustrated tale for younger readers who love high-seas adventure. Matilda sends for help from her best friend Jim Lad and his pirate family after raiders attack Matilda's seaside town, Dull-on-Sea.

It's Jim Lad's grandpa who reveals that the raiders are the worst rogues of all: undead ghost-pirates, led by the ruthless Twirlybeard. Matilda, who loves all things piratey (everything she wears is pirate-patterned), has the time of her life helping Jim Lad thwart Twirlybeard in a midnight adventure that brings them nose-to-nose with the bloodthirsty ghosts.

Jonny Duddle's illustrations are chock-full of personality, and readers will love his mash-ups between normal life and pirate life, like when Jim Lad's dad scrambles to find the email address of another pirate captain. A visual feast of a book.
■ *Sheila M Averbuch, Writer & Copywriter*

IF YOU LIKE THIS, WHY NOT TRY . . .

 FRIGHTFULLY FRIENDLY GHOSTIES: SCHOOL OF MEANIES
Daren King & David Roberts

 DAMIEN DROOTH SUPERSLEUTH: GRUESOME GHOST
Barbara Mitchelhill

CHILL
Alex Nye
(Floris)

When Samuel and his mum have to move into a new home in Sherrifmuir and are trapped by a heavy snowfall, he's lucky enough to make friends with Fiona Morton, one of the children who lives in the big, bleak and somewhat spooky Dunadd House.

The intrepid pair begin to peel away layers of history and uncover the curse that's blighted the Morton family for hundreds of years. Who is the ghostly, weeping figure that haunts the house? Is there any way they can help her and break an ancient curse?

We had to read this with the big light on! Full of surprises and great historical detail, it's a really exciting read. And Kai, aged nine, said, 'I would highly recommend this brilliant book and I loved the history. It was a real page turner but be warned: it is scary. My mum made me read it aloud to her as she had hid under the covers!'
■ *Hannah Lavery, Creative Director at Coastword and Kai's mum*

IF YOU LIKE THIS, WHY NOT TRY . . .

 THE GLASS CHILDREN
Kristina Ohlsson

 KNIGHTS OF THE BORROWED DARK
Dave Rudden

THE LIST

THE ROBE OF SKULLS
Vivian French & Ross Collins
(Walker)

The sorceress Lady Lamorna has her heart set on a creepy new robe in a Five Kingdom's adventure packed with magic, mischief, witches and trolls.

Who wants a new dress robe so badly they'd blackmail, kidnap and even use a little black magic to get it? Only someone as spooky as Lady Lamorna. Who is brave enough to stop her? Only the heroic Gracie Gillypot! With the help of a scruffy prince, a grudge-holding troll, the wickedest stepsister in the kingdom and some super chatty bats, it's up to Gracie to put a stop to Lamorna's mischief.

If you're bored of princes and princesses doing the same old thing, then the Tales from the Five Kingdom series is for you. *The Robe of Skulls* is the kind of fairy tale you can really get your teeth into – the heroes are awesome and the baddies are even better.
■ *Lynsey May, Writer & Copywriter*

IF YOU LIKE THIS, WHY NOT TRY . . .

 TALES OF TERROR FROM THE BLACK SHIP Chris Priestley

 THE GIRL WHO WASN'T THERE Karen McCombie

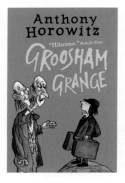

GROOSHAM GRANGE
Anthony Horowitz
(Walker)

When David is expelled from school for terrible grades, he is sent away to Groosham Grange, where a bad report card is the least of his fears. At Groosham, the French teacher is a werewolf, the assistant head is a vampire and the headmaster has more than just one head. Soon, David realises he'll be lucky to get out alive, never mind with full marks. There's definitely something very strange and rather nasty going on at this school - the question is, what's David going to do about it?

I loved this book when I read it at the end of primary school. It's perfect for anyone who has ever felt a little bit different or scared of fitting in. It's packed with some really good jokes, and even more terrible ones. It's funnier than Harry Potter, scarier than The Worst Witch, and sillier than David Walliams. If you want to read something hilariously horrible and horribly hilarious, this is the book for you.
■ *Simon Ewing, Bookseller at Waterstones*

IF YOU LIKE THIS, WHY NOT TRY . . .

 SCREAM STREET: FANG OF THE VAMPIRE Tommy Donbavand

 THE THORNWAITE INHERITANCE Gareth P Jones

THE WITCHES
Roald Dahl & Quentin Blake
(Penguin)

A fast-paced first-person fantasy, this book is full of scary suspense and humour. Dahl delights in sowing seeds of unease in his readers by making the ordinary extraordinary, encouraging them to look beyond the surface at what might lie beneath. This cautionary tale that appearances can be deceptive resonates with today's age of internet safety – and the message that you can love, be loved, be brave and carve out a successful career saving the world no matter your appearance, size or species will never date.

This is the first book I read which featured a heroic grandson/grandmother double act – a real cross-generational dynamic duo. Despite a great deal of character background, we never find out their names, giving the reader the impression that this is indeed a true story with our heroes' identities withheld to ensure their anonymity.

But, of course, it is just a fantastic fiction . . . there are no such things as Real Witches . . . are there?
■ *Katrina Lucas, Teacher*

IF YOU LIKE THIS, WHY NOT TRY . . .

 AWFUL AUNTIE
David Walliams

 THE NAME OF THIS BOOK IS SECRET
Pseudonymous Bosch

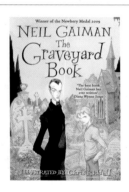

THE GRAVEYARD BOOK
Neil Gaiman & Chris Riddell
(Bloomsbury)

When a baby toddles into a close-knit community with a killer in pursuit, the local inhabitants protect him. Out of that act of charity, the simply unthinkable has occurred: the baby has been adopted by a graveyard!

Years pass as young Bod is taught how to live by the ghosts of shopkeepers, witches and poets. All the while, he is watched over by supernatural guardians with a mission to save the world from the same dark forces that orphaned him.

Told in episodic chunks, each heralded by Riddell's intricate and dramatic illustrations, this is a book that communicates its world with beautiful depth and clarity. What Kipling's *Jungle Book* roars about humanity's relationship with nature, *The Graveyard Book* whistles softly through the night about our relationship with death.

I was particularly touched to discover so many unsettling but endearing characters, delivering a story full of wry humour, tangible melancholy, and a passion for life.
■ *Nicole Brandon, Scottish Book Trust*

IF YOU LIKE THIS, WHY NOT TRY . . .

 LOCKWOOD & CO: THE SCREAMING STAIRCASE
Jonathan Stroud

 MOUNTWOOD SCHOOL FOR GHOSTS
Toby Ibbotson & Alex T Smith

ELF GIRL AND RAVEN BOY: FRIGHT FOREST
Marcus Sedgwick & Pete Williamson
(Orion)

When a tree falls in a forest and the only people around to hear it are a feather-flecked boy who talks to animals and a girl with pointed ears and a little bit of magic in her blood, does an adventure ensue? You bet it does.

The first story in this series takes Elf Girl and Raven Boy into the heart of Fright Forest in order to try and thwart an ogre who is destroying their home.

While dodging danger and becoming friends, they also pick up a few unexpected companions (and dastardly enemies) along the way, all beautifully punctuated by Pete Williamson's black and white ink-flood illustrations. After surviving Fright Forest, I'm sure you'll want to follow these two into all sorts of trouble as the books take them out into bigger, scarier and ever more exciting worlds.

■ *Candice Purwin, Illustrator & Comic Writer*

IF YOU LIKE THIS, WHY NOT TRY . . .

DOLL BONES
Holly Black

JIM REAPER: SON OF GRIM
Rachel Delahaye & Jamie Littler

SGEULACHDAN EAGALACH FEAGALACH
Catriona Lexy Chaimbeul & Johnny Stormonth-Darling
(Acair)

Bana-bhuidsich, sìthichean, troich, rìgh mosach agus bodach beag uaine – thig thu tarsaing orra uile anns na sgeulachdan goirid seo le Catrìona Lexy Chaimbeul.

Leugh mu dheidhinn Annabella àlainn a tha a' saoilsinn mòran dhith fhèin ged a tha i gu math mì-mhodhail ri na sgoilearan eile nuair nach eil duin' eile ga faicinn. Faigh a-mach mar a thug Peigi a' char às an rìgh mosach agus saoil dè a thachair nuair a choinnich Seonaidh bodach beag uaine anns a' choille?

Ma 's toigh leat sgeulachdan annasach, eagalach còrdaidh an leabhar seo riut. Mura cuir na caractaran oillteil anns an leabhar seo an t-eagal ort, cuiridh mi geall gun cuir na dealbhan dorcha aig Johnny Stormonth-Darling gaoir tro d' fheòil!

■ *Rosemary Ward, Director of the Comhairle nan Leabhraichean*

IF YOU LIKE THIS, WHY NOT TRY . . .

THE BEAST
Michaela Morgan & Chris Mould

ARAMINTA SPOOK: MY HAUNTED HOUSE
Angie Sage

Resources
For Readers

HOW PARENTS AND CARERS CAN HELP MAKE READING FUN

Helping children to fall in love with reading at home is just as important as what goes on at school. Here are some top tips to encourage them on their reading journey

■ Reading aloud to your children doesn't need to stop when they get older and, as long as it's something you both enjoy, it's a great way to appreciate a good story together.

■ Even if your child prefers to read on their own, take time to chat about what they are reading. It shows that you value their opinions and interests and builds their confidence.

■ Make reading a social experience with friends, siblings and relatives. Some children want to start mini book clubs to discuss books they are interested in or have a party based on a book they love.

■ Children will be more excited about reading if they can choose materials related to their interests. As well as contemporary novels and classics, encourage them to try graphic novels and magazines too. Give your

'Children are made readers on the laps of their parents'
- Emilie Buchwald

child the chance to discover what they like to read.

■ Visit the library regularly. Let your child choose their own book and use their own library card.

■ Be a role model. When children see members of their family reading frequently, discussing what they have read and carrying books around, they will value reading more.

■ Many children don't want to read simply because the books they encounter are too difficult or the themes or

'There are perhaps no days of our childhood we lived so fully as those we spent with a favourite book'

- Marcel Proust

language are not challenging enough. Ask your child if they feel the book is interesting and challenging and speak to their teacher for advice.

■ Take advantage of new technology. Reading texts on electronic readers, such as an iPad or Kindle can make it seem more engaging to children. There are also a number of fantastic apps to support struggling readers.

■ Help your child develop their vocabulary by using lots of different words when you speak to them. Talk about what new words mean and encourage your child to try using them.

■ Take a book everywhere you go and make up stories as you travel.

■ Encouraging children to share books with younger siblings or friends can make reading fun.

■ Have a special place to keep your books at home and make sure to put time aside to read them.

'I will defend the importance of bedtime stories to my last gasp'

- JK Rowling

MAKING THE MOST OF YOUR PUBLIC LIBRARY

There are more than 500 libraries across the country with a brilliant selection of reading materials for children, staffed by enthusiastic booklovers who would be happy to help your child choose. The 300 books suggested here are just the first page in the world of children's writing.

Libraries offer a great range of reading materials whatever a child's interests or reading ability. Every year, children in Scotland borrow over 6 million books from public libraries, including fiction, poetry, history, non-fiction, sports books, graphic novels, comics, audio books, apps and much more besides – we can help your child broaden their horizons.

Evidence shows that children who use their library and read regularly are more confident, develop strong language and literacy skills, have good concentration, develop empathy and achieve better attainment levels at school than those who have not developed a reading habit. Public libraries give every child equal access to a breadth of reading materials as they grow.

LIBRARIES AS A WONDERFUL READING CHALLENGE RESOURCE

The First Minister's Reading Challenge is a fantastic opportunity for public libraries to work with their local schools to encourage children in P4–7 to use their imagination, discover and explore a world of books and stories.

As part of the Challenge, librarians and teachers will be working together to encourage children to read widely and explore the world of books on their doorstep.

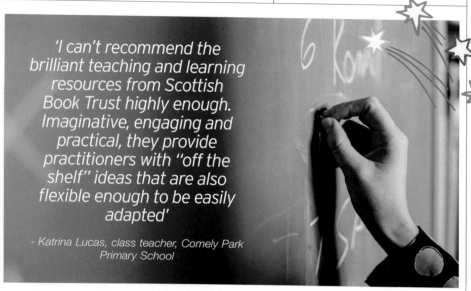

'I can't recommend the brilliant teaching and learning resources from Scottish Book Trust highly enough. Imaginative, engaging and practical, they provide practitioners with "off the shelf" ideas that are also flexible enough to be easily adapted'

- Katrina Lucas, class teacher, Comely Park Primary School

READING CHALLENGE:
SUPPORT FOR TEACHERS

Scottish Book Trust is sending every primary school in Scotland a Teachers' Pack, with sample materials and a guide to the First Minister's Reading Challenge for P4–7. This guide will include a number of ways you can get involved in the Challenge, tips for developing a reading culture in your school, details of prizes that are up for grabs, as well as suggestions on setting up library and community partnerships.

Once your school has registered, you will have access to the resources section of the website www.readingchallenge.scot/resources. You will find a whole range of free, downloadable support materials, such as templates, display activities, adaptable presentations and much more that you can use to support your class and develop a reading culture in your school. When you register you can request reading passports for all children taking part in the Challenge and download customisable certificates to reward your pupils' achievements.

We are helping to bring reading alive by opening a brand new author visits fund for schools taking part in the Challenge. This fund gives schools the chance to apply for a small grant for an author to visit their school and to buy books for the children taking part in the event. You can find details of the fund and how to apply on our website at www.readingchallenge.scot/InspiringClassrooms

The 300 titles in this publication are just the tip of the iceberg. On the website, you can browse through book lists compiled by a range of learning professionals, community members, organisations and children themselves. You can also create your own and submit it.

We have a range of support materials to help you begin your Reading Challenge journey, whether you're a school, library or individual as well as resources to help you continue to sustain your reading culture.

HOW COMMUNITIES CAN

Encouraging children to read for pleasure is not just for schools or parents and carers. When the wider community becomes actively involved, the benefits can be immense. Lindsey Barley, a deputy head teacher in East Lothian and champion of three community reading projects, shares her experiences of bringing the community together to encourage reading

'It all began five years ago with Dunbar Reads Together, a project based around the largest primary school in Scotland. I approached organisations who work with children and families, asking for help in two specific areas. Firstly, for help as Reading Champions to support individual children within their organisation who might not have another adult to read with. This led to rugby coaches reading with individuals after training sessions, Rainbow leaders sharing books with some of their children and the swimming club supporting members of the swim team. Volunteers from churches, the library service and staff within school, including our janitor, ensured no school child lacked support and encouragement from another adult when it came to reading.

'My second request was more ethereal – I needed help to create a reading culture in the town. None of us knew exactly what a reading culture would look like, but everyone was very enthusiastic. So began a wonderful and exciting journey. The Rotary Club donated a sofa which was placed on the High Street on Saturdays so

people could sit and read. The swimming pool hosted underwater reading sessions! East Coast trains donated a prize for children who wrote poems about reading, displaying the winning entries on posters throughout their network. The Brownies and the Rainbows all worked for their Reading Badges.

'As a key part of the project, children earned the right to wear a lanyard with a card detailing the book they were currently enjoying. All our supporters in the community wore a lanyard too, and these stimulated natural discussions about books and reading that became powerful tools. Children expect teachers and parents to

ENCOURAGE READING

Bees by Sue Monk Kidd, *Billionaire Boy* by David Walliams or *The Highway Rat* by Julia Donaldson and Axel Scheffler. We purchased copies to leave at locations around town and the library experienced high demand. People were encouraged to comment on the books on social media.

'We installed reading shelves at doctors' and dentists' surgeries, cafés, the train station and the swimming pool, filled with donated books to read and pass on.

'In this way a reading culture was developed in Dunbar. More people were reading and more people were talking about books. There was measurable positive impact in school with the P7 reading attainment rising by 12.5% in that year.

> *'A house without books is like a room without windows'*
>
> *- Heinrich Mann*

'Repeating the project in Tranent with nine schools including the secondary school, the community again responded with enthusiasm and energy. As well as adapting many of the previous ideas, adults came into schools to facilitate lunchtime reading sessions and schools joined together to hear visiting authors. We also created a beautiful patchwork quilt to represent all the books read.

'This year, Reading is Braw took place in Musselburgh, Wallyford and Whitecraig with over three thousand children. From pop-up libraries to "book bombing" sessions, a reading mile to a flash reading mob, the support was phenomenal.'

"nag" them to read, but suddenly the cool sports coaches were wearing lanyards and discussing books. In the local pizza restaurant, chip shop and coffee shops, waiters were chatting to children, and others, about what they were reading. The children were amazed and began to think about reading as an enjoyable experience rather than as a necessary requirement. Adults commented that they were reading more as they discussed recommendations from friends' lanyards.

'Working with local book groups, I encouraged everyone in the town to read one of three titles over the year: *The Secret Life of*

Creating community-wide involvement in reading is not an easy task, but the impact can be huge, whether from full-scale projects like these or taking the first steps in motivating young people to read for pleasure. Shared vision and enthusiasm for supporting our young people can and does change lives.

YOUR READING RECOMMENDATIONS

We hope the suggestions in this book have given you inspiration to start reading journeys of your own. Once you have begun to explore as an individual, a family or a class, why not make up your own list of books you love and share it with others?

We want to get people talking about reading in every Scottish town, city, village and house. To help start the conversation, we'd love to hear about your favourite children's books, whether you've read them yourself or you love reading them with children. Check out our celebrity recommendations and find out how to send us yours at www.readingchallenge.scot.

PICTURE BOOKS FOR OLDER READERS

Picture books are for everyone, from toddlers to adults. If you're an older reader, these books will give you a great reading experience, ranging from dark explorations of xenophobia to whimsical parodies of popular folk tales.

MOUSE, BIRD, SNAKE, WOLF
David Almond & Dave McKean
THE ISLAND
Armin Greder
THE MOST WONDERFUL THING IN THE WORLD
Vivian French
BLACK DOG
Levi Pinfold

FIREBIRD
Saviour Pirotta
JOURNEY
Aaron Becker
THIS IS NOT MY HAT
Jon Klassen

■ *List compiled by Cleo Jones, Manager for Information and Learning Resources in City of Edinburgh Council's Schools and Community Services Department.*

BOOKS ABOUT NUMBERS

The world wouldn't work without maths and numbers. From a playful look at where numbers came from, to a maths whizz trying to work out how to dodge PE and a schoolboy developing a business plan to make toothpaste, these titles make maths relevant and fun.

FROM ZERO TO TEN
Vivian French
MURDEROUS MATHS SERIES
Kjartan Poskitt
THE TOOTHPASTE MILLIONAIRE
Jean Merrill
THE MATH WIZ
Betsy Duffey

■ *List compiled by Making Maths Count, a Scottish Government initiative to encourage greater enthusiasm for maths among children and young people, their parents and carers and the wider public.*

INDEX (A to Z by book title)

The Accidental Time
Traveller 38
The Adventurs o TinTin:
The Derk Isle 55
Ancient to Modern: A Guide
to the History of the
Games – The Olympics 27
The Anti-Princess Club:
Bella's Backyard Bullies 28
Asterix and the Pechts 30
Baby Aliens Got
My Teacher................................. 14
Balach na Bonaid 21
Bear Grylls -
Mission Survival 58
Beetle Boy.................................. 50
Blamehounds 63
The Bolds................................... 64
A Boy Called Hope.................... 44
Cakes in Space 56
Camp Gold................................. 24
Charlie Merrick's Misfits:
Fouls, Friends and Football........ 27
Chill 67
The Chronicles of Narnia:
The Lion the Witch and
the Wardrobe 57
Circus of Thieves and
The Raffle of Doom 12
Claude in the City...................... 60
Corpse Talk: Season 1 32
Cosmic...................................... 42
Daisy: The Trouble with
Sports Day 25
Danger is Everywhere! 14
The Day the Crayons Quit 13
The Day the World went Loki 49
Deadly!: The Truth About
The Most Dangerous
Creatures on Earth
(Animal Science)........................ 64
Demolition Dad.......................... 45
Disgusting Science.................... 15
The Dragon Stoorworm 21
Dreamsnatcher.......................... 36
Evil Emperor Penguin 48
The Famous Five........................ 37
The Fish in the Bathtub 33
Flying Fergus: The Best
Birthday Bike 24

Freddie Mole: Lion Tamer 63
George's Secret Key to the
Universe 58
The Ghostly Galleon 67
The Girl Who Circumnavigated
Fairyland in a Ship of her Own
Making 19
Goth Girl and the Ghost
of a Mouse 66
The Graveyard Book 69
Groosham Grange..................... 68
The Gruffalo in Scots................. 61
Harry Potter............................... 40
Horrid Henry's Jumbo
Joke Book.................................. 13
How to Train Your Dragon 54
In Darkling Wood....................... 20
Ink Heart 37
Katie Morag and the
Two Grandmothers.................... 45
Lollipop and Grandpa
Go Swimming............................ 26
Long Gone Don.......................... 48
Looking Glass Girl 43
Love That Dog............................ 60
Manfred the Baddie................... 52
Marsh Road Mysteries:
Diamonds and Dagger 36
Mary Queen of Scots
and All That 31
Moone Boy................................. 42
Mr Mingin (Mr Stink in Scots).... 12
Mr Mumbles – Invisible Fiends... 66
Murder Most Unladylike............. 39
My Brother is a Superhero......... 52
The Mysteries of
Ravenstorm Island series........... 38
The Nowhere Emporium............. 55
Once 33
One Dog and his Boy................. 56
The Orchard Book of
Aesop's Fables 22
Osbert The Avenger 50
Out of Clouds............................ 46
Peter Pan (Graphic Novel) 18
The Princess in Black 51
The Prince Who
Walked With Lions..................... 31
Raven Boy and Elf Girl.............. 70
The Robe of Skulls 68

Roodica the Rude and
the Famous Flea Trick 16
Rugby Academy:
Combat Zone 25
The Runner 44
The Savage 43
The Secret of the Kelpie............ 18
Sgeulachdan Eagalach
Feagalach.................................. 70
Shackleton's Journey 54
The Shapeshifter:
Feather and Fang 58
Skyhawk..................................... 62
A Slightly Jones Mystery:
The Case of the Glasgow Ghoul 34
Soldier's Game 28
Stars Shall Be Bright 34
Stinky Cheese Man
(and Other Fairly Stupid Tales) ..20
A Tale Dark & Grimm................. 22
The Thieves of Ostia................. 30
Thorfinn the Nicest Viking.......... 51
Tiger Wars.................................. 62
Tom Gates................................. 16
The Unbelievable Top
Secret Diary of Pig.................... 61
Vile's Vengeance (Atomic!) 49
Weird World of Wonders
(Egyptians)................................ 32
What to do About Holly? 46
Who's Afraid of the
Big Bad Book?.......................... 19
Witch Baby and Me.................. 40
Witch Wars................................ 39
The Witches 69
The World of Norm:
May Contain Nuts...................... 25
You Tell Me................................ 15

INDEX (A to Z by author, illustrator or translator)